Arthur

She
Holmes
stories

Sir **Arthur Conan Doyle** (1859 – 1930) was educated at Edinburgh and practised medicine as a profession. He is remembered chiefly for his creation of the amateur detective, Sherlock Holmes, embodied in a cycle of stories (*The Adventures of Sherlock Holmes*, 1891; *The Memories of Sherlock Holmes*, 1894; *The Hound of the Baskervilles*, 1902, and others) and of his friend and foil Dr. Watson with whom he shares rooms in Baker Street.

Holmes became so popular that, when in 1893 Conan Doyle, tired of his character, tried to get rid of start him, the reaction of the public was so strong that he had to star a new series of Holmes Adventures.

Doyle's first work of fiction, *A Study in Scarlet*, (also a Holmes story) appeared in 1887 and was followed by a series of historical and other novels for half a century.

Among the most noteworthy are *Micah Clarke* (1889); *The White Company* (1891); *The Exploits of Brigadier Gerard* (1896); *Rodney Stone* (1896) and *The Lost World* (1912), which was the first of the stories featuring Professor Challenger, a distinguished zoologist and anthropologist of great vitality and violent temper.

In 1926 he wrote a *History of Spiritualism*, a subject in which he was much interested during his later years.

La Spiga
LANGUAGES

A Case of Identity

"My dear fellow, " said Sherlock Holmes, as we sat on either side of the fire in his lodgings at Baker Street, "life is infinitely stranger than anything which the mind of man could invent. We would not dare to conceive the things which are really mere commonplaces of existence. If we could fly out of that window hand in hand, hover over this great city, gently remove the roofs, and peep in at the queer things which are going on, the strange coincidences, the plannings, the cross-purposes, the wonderful chains of events, working through generations, and leading to the most *outré* results, it would make all fiction with its conventionalities and foreseen conclusions most stale and unprofitable."

"And yet I am not convinced of it," I answered. "The cases which come to light in the papers are, as a rule, bald enough, and vulgar enough. We have in our police reports realism pushed to its extreme limits, and yet the result is, it must be confessed, neither fascinating nor artistic."

"A certain selection and discretion must be used in producing a realistic effect, " remarked Holmes. "This is wanting

fellow: man, friend. **as**: when.
lodgings: flat; apartment.

would not dare: would not have the courage. **to conceive**: to imagine. **mere**: only. **commonplaces**: ordinary facts.
hover: be suspended in flight.
peep in: observe secretly. **queer**: strange.
going on: happening.
cross-purposes: contrary purposes. **chains**: series.
leading: taking.
outré: unusual; bizarre. **fiction**: novels; stories.
foreseen: predictable. **most**: very. **stale**: unexciting; uninteresting. **unprofitable**: not worth reading.

come to light: are reported. **papers**: newspapers. **as a rule**: generally. **bald**: frank.
pushed to: taken to.
neither ... nor ...: structure used to join together two negative ideas. **discretion**: judgement.
remarked: said; observed. **is wanting**: is not present.

in the police report, where more stress is laid perhaps upon the platitudes of the magistrate than upon the details, which to an observer contain the vital essence of the whole matter.

Depend upon it there is nothing so unnatural as the commonplace. "

I smiled and shook my head. "I can quite understand you thinking so," I said. "Of course, in your position of unofficial adviser and helper to everybody who is absolutely puzzled, throughout three continents, you are brought in contact with all that is strange and bizarre. But here" – I picked up the morning paper from the ground – "let us put it to a practical test. Here is the first heading upon which I come. 'A husband's cruelty to his wife.' There is half a column of print, but I know without reading it that it is all perfectly familiar to me. There is, of course, the other woman, the drink, the push, the blow, the bruise, the sympathetic sister or landlady. The crudest of writers could invent nothing more crude."

"Indeed, your example is an unfortunate one for your argument," said Holmes, taking the paper, and glancing his eye down it. "This is the Dundas separation case, and, as it happens, I was engaged in clearing up some small points in connection with it. The husband was a teetotaller, there was no other woman, and the conduct complained of was that he had drifted into the habit of winding up every meal by taking out his false teeth and hurling them at his wife, which you will allow is not an action likely to occur to the imagination of the average story-teller. Take a pinch of snuff, Doctor, and acknowledge that I have scored over you in your example."

He held out his snuff-box of old gold, with a great amethyst in the centre of the lid. Its splendour was in such contrast to his homely ways and simple life that I could not help commenting upon it.

"Ah," said he, "I forgot that I had not seen you for some weeks. It is a little souvenir from the King of Bohemia in return for my assistance in the case of the Irene Adler

stress: importance. **perhaps**: maybe. **upon**: (archaic) on.
platitudes: dull observations. **upon**: on. **details**: facts.
to an observer: to the mind of an observer. **whole**: entire.
matter: affair.
Depend upon it: put your trust in it; believe it.
commonplace: ordinary facts.
shook my head: moved my head as to say "no".
Of course: certainly.
adviser: counsellor.
puzzled: confused. **throughout**: through the whole of.

paper: newspaper. **ground**: floor.
heading: headline; title. **upon**: (archaic) on.

print: printed words.
of course: obviously.
the push: the assault. **the blow**: the hit with the fist. **the bruise**:
the wound; the injury. **sympathetic**: compassionate. **landlady**:
owner of the house. **crudest**: grossest.
Indeed: certainly; actually.
paper: newspaper.
glancing his eye down it: looking quickly at it.
as it happens: coincidentally. **I was engaged**: I participated.
was a teetotaller: didn't drink at all.
conduct: behaviour. **complained of**: taken before justice.
had drifted into the habit: had started the habit. **winding up**:
finishing; concluding. **taking out**: removing. **hurling**: throwing.
allow: admit. **likely**: probable.
occur to the imagination: come forth out of the imagination.
average: typical. **story-teller**: author. **snuff**: tobacco for smelling.
acknowledge: admit. **scored over you**: beaten you.
amethyst: precious stone.
lid: cover.
homely ways: simple manners. **help**: avoid.

I had not seen you: *duration form*.

in return: in exchange; in gratitude. **assistance**: help.

papers."

"And the ring?" I asked, glancing at a remarkable brilliant which sparkled upon his finger.

"It was from the reigning family of Holland, though the matter in which I served them was of such delicacy that I cannot confide it even to you, who have been good enough to chronicle one or two of my little problems."

"And have you any on hand just now?" I asked with interest.

"Some ten or twelve, but none which presents any feature of interest. They are important, you understand, without being interesting. Indeed, I have found that it is usually in unimportant matters that there is a field for observation, and for the quick analysis of cause and effect which gives the charm to an investigation. The larger crimes are apt to be the simpler, for the bigger the crime, the more obvious, as a rule, is the motive. In these cases, save for one rather intricate matter which has been referred to me from Marseilles, there is nothing which presents any features of interest. It is possible, however, that I may have something better before very many minutes are over, for this is one of my clients, or I am much mistaken."

He had risen from his chair, and was standing between the parted blinds, gazing down into the dull, neutral-tinted London street. Looking over his shoulder I saw that on the pavement opposite there stood a large woman with a heavy fur boa round her neck, and a large curling red feather in a broad-brimmed hat which was tilted in a coquettish Duchess-of-Devonshire fashion over her ear. From under this great panoply she peeped up in a nervous, hesitating fashion at our windows, while her body oscillated backwards and forwards, and her fingers fidgeted with her glove buttons. Suddenly, with a plunge, as of the swimmer who leaves the bank, she hurried across the road, and we heard the sharp clang of the bell.

"I have seen those symptoms before," said Holmes, throwing his cigarette into the fire. "Oscillation upon the pavement always means an *affaire du coeur*. She would like

papers: documents.
glancing: looking. **remarkable**: impressive. **brilliant**: diamond.
sparkled: reflected light. **upon**: (archaic) on.
though: even if.
the matter: the affair; the case.
confide: reveal.
to chronicle: to record.
on hand: at present; available.

Some: about. **feature**: aspect; characteristic.

indeed: actually.
matters: situations. **a field for observation**: anything worth looking into.
charm: interest. **are apt**: are likely.

as a rule: generally. **motive**: reason. **save for**: except for.

features: details; particulars.
however: anyway. **I may have**: *may* expresses possibility.
are over: are passed. **for**: because.
I am much mistaken: I am quite wrong.
He had risen: he had stood up.
parted: open. **blinds**: shades of the window. **gazing**: looking.
dull: grey.
pavement: walkway for pedestrians.
fur boa: feathery scarf. **curling**: twisting.
broad-brimmed: with a wide brim. **tilted**: inclined. **coquettish**: intending to attract men's attention. **fashion**: way; manner.
panoply: magnificent covering. **peeped up**: looked up.
fashion: way.
fidgeted: played nervously.
plunge: jump.
bank: land edge by a river. **hurried**: moved quickly.
clang: ringing.

advice, but is not sure that the matter is not too delicate for communication. And yet even here we may discriminate. When a woman has been seriously wronged by a man she no longer oscillates, and the usual symptom is a broken bell wire. Here we may take it that there is a love matter, but that the maiden is not so much angry as perplexed, or grieved. But here she comes in person to resolve our doubts."

As he spoke there was a tap at the door, and the boy in buttons entered to announce Miss Mary Sutherland, while the lady herself loomed behind his small black figure like a full-sailed merchantman behind a tiny pilot boat. Sherlock Holmes welcomed her with the easy courtesy for which he was remarkable, and having closed the door, and bowed her into an arm-chair, he looked over her in the minute and yet abstracted fashion which was peculiar to him.

"Do you not find, " he said, "that with your short sight it is a little trying to do so much typewriting?"

"I did at first," she answered, "but now I know where the letters are without looking." Then, suddenly realizing the full purport of his words, she gave a violent start, and looked up with fear and astonishment upon her broad, good-humoured face. "You've heard about me, Mr. Holmes," she cried, "else how could you know all that?"

"Never mind, " said Holmes, laughing, "it is my business to know things. Perhaps I have trained myself to see what others overlook. If not, why should you come to consult me?"

"I came to you, sir, because I heard of you from Mrs. Etherege, whose husband you found so easy when the police and everyone had given him up for dead. Oh, Mr. Holmes, I wish you would do as much for me. I'm not rich, but still I have a hundred a year in my own right, besides the little that I make by the machine, and I would give it all to know what has become of Mr. Hosmer Angel."

"Why did you come away to consult me in such a hurry?" asked Sherlock Holmes, with his finger-tips together, and his eyes to the ceiling.

advice: counsel. **matter**: situation.

for communication: to be communicated.

wronged: treated wrongly.

no longer: no more.

bell wire: cord connected to the bell. **may take it**: may assume.

matter: question; problem. **maiden**: girl; unmarried woman.

grieved: sad. **resolve**: solve; clear.

As: while. **tap**: knock.

the boy in buttons: the page.

herself: in person. **loomed**: stood bigger than him.

full-sailed: with every sail set. **merchantman**: ship used in commerce. **tiny**: small. **pilot boat**: boat that takes ships in and out of the port. **easy**: nice. **remarkable**: especially known.

minute: accurate; precise.

fashion: way; manner.

find: think. **with your short sight**: being unable to see distant things. **a little trying**: somewhat difficult.

at first: initially.

realizing: understanding.

purport: implication. **start**: motion.

astonishment: great surprise. **upon**: on. **broad**: wide.

good-humoured: cheerful.

cried: shouted. **else**: otherwise.

Never mind: don't worry about that. **business**: profession.

trained: taught; educated.

overlook: pass over.

so easy: so easily; without much effort.

had given him up for dead: had considered him dead.

I wish you would do: note the tense after *to wish*.

in my own right: belonging personally to me. **besides**: in addition to this. **by the machine**: typewriting.

has become of: has happened to.

in such a hurry: so hastily.

ceiling: roof of the room.

Again a startled look came over the somewhat vacuous face of Miss Mary Sutherland. "Yes, I did bang out of the house," she said, "for it made me angry to see the easy way in which Mr. Windibank – that is, my father – took it all. He would not go to the police, and he would not go to you, and so at last, as he would do nothing, and kept on saying that there was no harm done, it made me mad, and I just on with my things and came right away to you."

"Your father?" said Holmes. "Your stepfather, surely, since the name is different?"

"Yes, my stepfather. I call him father, though it sounds funny, too, for he is only five years and two months older than myself."

"And your mother is alive?"

"Oh, yes, mother is alive and well. I wasn't best pleased, Mr. Holmes, when she married again so soon after father's death, and a man who was nearly fifteen years younger than herself. Father was a plumber in the Tottenham Court Road, and he left a tidy business behind him, which mother carried on with Mr. Hardy, the foreman, but when Mr. Windibank came he made her sell the business, for he was very superior, being a traveller in wines. They got four thousand seven hundred for the goodwill and interest, which wasn't near as much as father could have got if he had been alive."

I had expected to see Sherlock Holmes impatient under this rambling and inconsequential narrative, but, on the contrary, he had listened with the greatest concentration of attention.

"Your own little income, " he asked, "does it come out of the business ?"

'Oh, no, sir, it is quite separate, and was left me by my Uncle Ned in Auckland. It is in New Zealand Stock, paying 4 $\frac{1}{2}$ per cent. Two thousand five hundred pounds was the amount, but I can only touch the interest."

"You interest me extremely," said Holmes. "And since you draw so large a sum as a hundred a year, with what you earn into the bargain, you no doubt travel a little and

startled: very surprised. **somewhat**: rather. **vacuous**: empty.
I did bang: *to do* is used emphatically. **bang out**: run out.
easy: not concerned.
took it all: was affected by it all.
He would not go: he did not intend to go.
at last: in the end. **would do**: wanted to do. **kept on saying**: said
repeatedly. **no harm**: no damage. **mad**: very angry.
I just on with my things: I just got dressed. **right away**: immediately. **stepfather**: mother's second husband.

though: even if.
funny: strange. **for**: because.

And your mother is alive?: the structure is not interrogative
because the question expects an affirmative answer. **well**: in
good health. **I wasn't best pleased**: I wasn't very happy.
nearly: almost.
was a plumber: installed and repaired water pipes. **the Tottenham Court Road**: the use of the article is *dialectal*. **tidy**: good;
successful. **behind him**: after his death. **carried on**: continued.
the foreman: the supervisor. **for**: because.
a traveller: commercial traveller; salesman. **they got**: they were
paid. **goodwill**: reputation.
near: nearly.

rambling: unconnected. **inconsequential**: unimportant.
on the contrary: note the preposition *on*.

your own little income: the small amount of money you receive.

amount: total; sum.

draw: earn.
into the bargain: in addition to that.

indulge yourself in every way. I believe that a single lady can get on very nicely upon an income of about sixty pounds."

"I could do with much less than that, Mr. Holmes, but you understand that as long as I live at home I don't wish to be a burden to them, and so they have the use of the money just while I am staying with them. Of course that is only just for the time. Mr. Windibank draws my interest every quarter, and pays it over to mother, and I find that I can do pretty well with what I earn at typewriting. It brings me twopence a sheet, and I can often do from fifteen to twenty sheets in a day."

"You have made your position very clear to me," said Holmes. "This is my friend, Dr. Watson, before whom you can speak as freely as before myself. Kindly tell us now all about your connection with Mr. Hosmer Angel."

A flush stole over Miss Sutherland's face, and she picked nervously at the fringe of her jacket. "I met him first at the gasfitters' ball," she said. "They used to send father tickets when he was alive, and then afterwards they remembered us, and sent them to mother. Mr. Windibank did not wish us to go. He never did wish us to go anywhere. He would get quite mad if I wanted so much as to join a Sunday school treat. But this time I was set on going, and I would go, for what right had he to prevent? He said the folk were not fit for us to know, when all father's friends were to be there. And he said that I had nothing fit to wear, when I had my purple plush that I had never so much as taken out of the drawer. At last, when nothing else would do, he went off to France upon the business of the firm, but we went, mother and I, with Mr. Hardy, who used to be our foreman, and it was there I met Mr. Hosmer Angel."

"I suppose," said Holmes, "that when Mr. Windibank came back from France, he was very annoyed at your having gone to the ball."

"Oh, well, he was very good about it. He laughed, I remember, and shrugged his shoulders, and said there was no use denying anything to a woman, for she would have

indulge yourself in every way: spend money for your own pleasure. **single**: unmarried. **get on**: live. **upon an income**: with an earning.

I could do: I could live.

at home: with my parents. **wish**: desire.

burden: financial expense.

just for the time: temporarily. **draws**: gets. **every quarter**: every three months.

It brings me: with it I earn.

before whom: in front of whom.

before myself: in front of me.

connection: relationship.

flush: red colour. **stole**: came.

fringe: edge. **first**: for the first time.

gasfitters' ball: ball of the men who install and repair gas pipes.

they used to send: they usually sent. **afterwards**: after his death.

did not wish us to go: note the *infinitive structure*.

quite mad: very angry. **so much as**: even to. **join**: take part in.

Sunday school treat: Church school entertainment. **I was set on going**: I was determined to go. **for**: because. **to prevent**: not to allow me to go. **folk**: people. **not fit for us to know**: note the *infinitive structure*. **fit**: good.

plush: fancy dress. **so much as**: even.

At last: in the end. **nothing else would do**: none of these objections were obeyed. **he went off**: left. **upon the business of the firm**: on business for the firm. **used to be**: in the past was.

foreman: supervisor.

annoyed: upset.

at your having gone: note the *construction*.

shrugged: lifted, raised.

there was no use: it was useless. **denying**: not allowing.

her way."

"I see. Then at the gasfitters' ball you met, as I understand, a gentleman called Mr. Hosmer Angel."

"Yes, sir. I met him that night, and he called next day to ask if we had got home all safe, and after that we met him – that is to say, Mr. Holmes, I met him twice for walks, but after that father came back again, and Mr. Hosmer Angel could not come to the house any more."

"No?"

"Well, you know, father didn't like anything of the sort. He wouldn't have any visitors if he could help it, and he used to say that a woman should be happy in her own family circle. But then, as I used to say to mother, a woman wants her own circle to begin with, and I had not got mine yet".

"But how about Mr. Hosmer Angel? Did he make no attempt to see you?"

"Well, father was going off to France again in a week, and Hosmer wrote and said that it would be safer and better not to see each other until he had gone. We could write in the meantime, and he used to write every day. I took the letters in in the morning so there was no need for father to know.

"Were you engaged to the gentleman at this time?"

"Oh yes, Mr. Holmes. We were engaged after the first walk that we took. Hosmer – Mr. Angel – was a cashier in an office in Leadenhall Street – and –"

"What office?"

"That's the worst of it, Mr. Holmes, I don't know."

"Where did he live then?"

"He slept on the premises."

"And you don't know his address?"

"No – except that it was Leadenhall Street."

"Where did you address your letters, then?"

"To the Leadenhall Street Post Office, to be left till called for. He said that if they were sent to the office he would be chaffed by all the other clerks about having letters from a lady, so I offered to typewrite them, like he did his, but he wouldn't have that, for he said that when I wrote them they seemed to come from me but when they were typewritten

would have her way: would do as she pleased.

gasfitters' ball: ball of the men who installed and repaired gas pipes.

next day: the next day.

safe: safely; without harm.

twice: two times. **for walks**: for walking together.

of the sort: of that kind.

wouldn't have: preferred not to have. **help**: avoid.

he used to say: he usually said.

I used to say: I usually said.

wants: needs.

how about: what of.

Did he make no attempt: did he not try.

going off to: leaving for.

safer: more secure.

meantime: meanwhile. **he used to write**: he had the habit of writing. **took the letters in**: took the letters into the house.

engaged to: promised to be married by. **at this time**: when this happened.

on the premises: at the same place where he worked.

address: send.

to be left: to stay there.

called for: requested.

chaffed: ridiculed. **clerks**: co-workers.

he wouldn't have that: he didn't allow that. **for**: because.

he always felt that the machine had come between us. That will just show you how fond he was of me, Mr. Holmes, and the little things that he would think of."

"It was most suggestive, " said Holmes. "It has long been an axiom of mine that the little things are infinitely the most important. Can you remember any other little things about Mr. Hosmer Angel?"

"He was a very shy man, Mr. Holmes. He would rather walk with me in the evening than in the daylight, for he said that he hated to be conspicuous. Very retiring and gentlemanly he was. Even his voice was gentle. He'd had the quinsy and swollen glands when he was young, he told me, and it had left him with a weak throat, and a hesitating, whispering fashion of speech. He was always well-dressed, very neat and plain, but his eyes were weak, just as mine are, and he wore tinted glasses against the glare."

"Well, and what happened when Mr. Windibank, your stepfather, returned to France?"

"Mr. Hosmer Angel came to the house again, and proposed that we should marry before father came back. He was in dreadful earnest, and made me swear, with my hands on the Testament, that whatever happened I would always be true to him. Mother said he was quite right to make me swear, and that it was a sign of his passion. Mother was all in his favour from the first, and was even fonder of him than I was. Then, when they talked of marrying within the week, I began to ask about father; but they both said never to mind about father, but just to tell him afterwards, and mother said she would make it all right with him. I didn't quite like that, Mr. Holmes. It seemed funny that I should ask his leave, as he was only a few years older than me, but I didn't want to do anything on the sly, so I wrote to father at Bordeaux, where the Company has its French office, but the letter came back to me on the very morning of the wedding"

"It missed him then?"

"Yes, sir, for he had started to England just before it arrived."

felt: had the impression.
just: exactly. **how fond he was of me**: how much affection he had for me.
most: very. **suggestive**: interesting. **It has long been**: *duration form*. **long**: for a long time. **axiom**: belief.

shy: timid. **he would rather**: he preferred to.
for: because.
to be conspicuous: to draw attention. **retiring**: modest.
gentle: delicate.
quinsy: tonsillitis.

whispering: talking in a low voice. **fashion**: manner.
neat: tidy; clean. **plain**: simple.   **just**: exactly.
tinted glasses: dark glasses. **glare**: light.

stepfather: mother's second husband.

dreadful: great. **earnest**: seriousness. **swear**: promise solemnly. **Testament**: Bible. **whatever**: no matter what.
true: faithful.
swear: promise.
was all in his favour: liked him very much. **from the first**: from the beginning. **was even fonder of him than I was**: liked him even more than I did.
never to mind: not to worry. **just**: only.
afterwards: after the marriage. **she would make**: *future in the past*.   **all right**: agreeable. **quite**: at all.
funny: strange. **leave**: permission.
than me: than I am. **on the sly**: secretly.

the very: the same.
wedding: ceremony.
missed: did not reach.
for: because. **started to**: begun his travel to; departed for.

"Ha! that was unfortunate. Your wedding was arranged, then, for the Friday. Was it to be in church?"

"Yes, sir, but very quietly. It was to be at St. Saviour's, near King's Cross, and we were to have breakfast afterwards at the St. Pancras Hotel. Hosmer came for us in a hansom, but as there were two of us, he put us both into it, and stepped himself into a four-wheeler which happened to be the only other cab in the street. We got to the church first, and when the four-wheeler drove up we waited for him to step out, but he never did, and when the cabman got down from the box and looked, there was no one there! The cabman said he could not imagine what had become of him, for he had seen him get in with his own eyes. That was last Friday, Mr. Holmes, and I have never seen or heard anything since then to throw any light upon what became of him."

"It seems to me that you have been very shamefully treated," said Holmes.

"Oh no sir! He was too good and kind to leave me so. Why, all the morning he was saying to me that, whatever happened, I was to be true; and that even if something quite unforeseen occurred to separate us, I was always to remember that I was pledged to him, and that he would claim his pledge sooner or later. It seemed strange talk for a wedding morning, but what has happened since gives a meaning to it."

"Most certainly it does. Your own opinion is, then, that some unforeseen catastrophe has occurred to him?"

"Yes, sir, I believe that he foresaw some danger, or else he would not have talked so. And then I think that what he foresaw happened."

"But you have no notion as to what it could have been?"

"None."

"One more question. How did your mother take the matter?"

"She was angry, and said that I was never to speak of the matter again."

"And your father? Did you tell him?"

"Yes, and he seemed to think, with me, that something had

arranged: planned.

Was it to be: was it planned to be.

It was to be: it was planned to be. **St. Saviour's**: St. Saviour's Church. **were to have**: were supposed to have. **afterwards**: after that. **came for us**: came to take us. **hansom**: two-wheeled horse drawn carriage. **stepped**: went.

four-wheeler: four-wheeled carriage. **happened to be**: coincidentally was. **cab**: vehicle for hire.

drove up: arrived. **waited for him to step out**: note the *infinitive structure* with *to wait for*. **cabman**: driver of the cab.

box: driving place.

had become of him: had happened to him. **for**: because.

his own: *own* intensifies the possessive.

upon: (archaic) on. **became of**: happened to.

shamefully: offensively.

leave: abandon. **so**: this way.

whatever: no matter what.

I was to: I had to. **true**: faithful. **quite**: completely.

unforeseen: unexpected. **occurred**: happened. **I was**: I had.

I was pledged to him: I was promised to him.

claim: demand; return to collect. **pledge**: promise. **sooner of later**: either in the near or in the distant future. **strange talk**: unusual conversation.

Most certainly: very surely; indeed.

unforeseen: unexpected. **occurred**: happened.

foresaw: predicted. **else**: otherwise.

foresaw: predicted.

no notion: no idea; no supposition.

the matter: the events; the affair.

I was never to speak: I should never speak.

the matter: the affair; the happenings.

happened, and that I should hear of Hosmer again. As he said, what interest could anyone have in bringing me to the doors of the church, and then leaving me? Now, if he had borrowed my money, or if he had married me and got my money settled on him, there might be some reason; but Hosmer was very independent about money, and never would look at a shilling of mine. And yet what could have happened? And why could he not write? Oh, it drives me half mad to think of it! and I can't sleep a wink at night." She pulled a little handkerchief out of her muff, and began to sob heavily into it.

"I shall glance into the case for you," said Holmes, rising, "and I have no doubt that we shall reach some definite result. Let the weight of the matter rest upon me now, and do not let your mind dwell upon it further. Above all, try to let Mr. Hosmer Angel vanish from your memory, as he has done from your life."

"Then you don't think I'll see him again?"

"I fear not."

"Then what has happened to him?"

"You will leave that question in my hands. I should like an accurate description of him, and any letters of his which you can spare."

"I advertised for him in last Saturday's *Chronicle*," said she.

"Here is the slip, and here are four letters from him."

"Thank you. And your address?"

"31 Lyon Place, Camberwell."

"Mr. Angel's address you never had, I understand. Where is your father's place of business?"

"He travels for Westhouse & Marbank, the great claret importers of Fenchurch Street."

"Thank you. You have made your statement very clearly. You will leave the papers here, and remember the advice which I have given you. Let the whole incident be a sealed book, and do not allow it to affect your life."

"You are very kind, Mr. Holmes, but I cannot do that. I shall be true to Hosmer. He shall find me ready when he

I should hear: *future in the past*.

leaving me: abandoning me.

settled on him: transferred to him.

half mad: almost crazy. **I can't sleep a wink**: I can't sleep even for a short time. **muff**: handwarmer.
to sob: to cry. **heavily**: much.
glance: look. **rising**: standing up.

weight: concern; worry. **matter**: affair.
dwell upon it: think about it. **further**: any longer.
vanish: disappear.

I fear not: I am afraid not.

accurate: detailed.
you can spare: you can give me.
advertised for him: published a notice looking for him.

slip: piece of paper.

of business: of work.
He travels: he is an agent.
claret importers: importers of wine.
statement: story.
papers: documents. **advice**: counsel.
whole: entire.
a sealed book: a closed book. **affect your life**: have influence on your life.
true: faithful.

comes back."

For all the preposterous hat and the vacuous face, there was something noble in the simple faith of our visitor which compelled our respect. She laid her little bundle of papers upon the table, and went her way, with a promise to come again whenever she might be summoned.

Sherlock Holmes sat silent for a few minutes with his finger-tips still pressed together, his legs stretched out in front of him, and his gaze directed upwards to the ceiling. Then he took down from the rack the old and oily clay pipe, which was to him as a counsellor, and, having lit it he leaned back in his chair, with the thick blue cloudwreaths spinning up from him, and a look of infinite languor in his face.

"Quite an interesting study, that maiden," he observed. "I found her more interesting than her little problem, which, by the way, is rather a trite one. You will find parallel cases, if you consult my index, in Andover in '77, and there was something of the sort at The Hague last year. Old as is the idea, however, there were one or two details which were new to me. But the maiden herself was most instructive."

"You appeared to read a good deal upon her which was quite invisible to me," I remarked.

"Not invisible, but unnoticed, Watson. You did not know where to look, and so you missed all that was important. I can never bring you to realize the importance of sleeves, the suggestiveness of thumb-nails, or the great issues that may hang from a bootlace. Now what did you gather from that woman's appearance? Describe it."

"Well, she had a slate-coloured, broad-brimmed straw hat, with a feather of a brickish red. Her jacket was black, with black beads sewn upon it, and a fringe of little black jet ornaments. Her dress was brown, rather darker than coffee colour, with a little purple plush at the neck and sleeves. Her gloves were greyish, and were worn through at the right forefinger. Her boots I didn't observe. She had small, round, hanging gold ear-rings, and a general air of being

preposterous: ridiculous. **vacuous**: empty.

compelled: inspired. **bundle**: package. **papers**: documents.
upon: (archaic) on.
whenever: at any time. **summoned**: called.

stretched out: extended.
gaze: look. **ceiling**: roof of the room.
rack: support.
counsellor: adviser.
leaned back: reclined back. **cloudwreaths**: smoke rings.
spinning up: spiralling.

maiden: unmarried woman.

by the way: incidentally. **trite**: uninteresting.
index: records.
of the sort: of that kind.
however: anyway. **details**: particulars.
maiden: unmarried girl. **herself**: personally. **most**: very.
instructive: enlightening.
You appeared to read: it seems that you have read. **deal**:
quantity. **quite**: completely. **remarked**: observed.

missed: overlooked; failed to see.
bring you to: make you. **realize**: understand.
suggestiveness: implication. **thumb-nails**: the nails of the first
finger. **issues**: information. **bootlace**: string of the boots. **gather**:
deduce. **appearance**: aspect.
slate-coloured: dark grey.
brickish: colour of the brick; dark orange.
fringe: edge. **black jet**: shiny black.

plush: fabric softer than velvet.
greyish: almost grey. **worn through**: deteriorated.
forefinger: index finger.

fairly well to do, in a vulgar, comfortable, easy-going way."

Sherlock Holmes clapped his hands softly together and chuckled.

"'Pon my word, Watson, you are coming along wonderfully. You have really done very well indeed. It is true that you have missed everything of importance, but you have hit upon the method, and you have a quick eye for colour. Never trust to general impressions, my boy, but concentrate yourself upon details. My first glance is always at a woman's sleeve. In a man it is perhaps better first to take the knee of the trouser. As you observe, this woman had plush upon her sleeves, which is a most useful material for showing traces. The double line a little above the wrist, where the typewritist presses against the table, was beautifully defined. The sewing-machine, of the hand type, leaves a similar mark, but only on the left arm, and on the side of it farthest from the thumb, instead of being right across the broadest part, as this was. I then glanced at her face, and observing the dint of a pince-nez at either side of her nose, I ventured a remark upon short sight and typewriting, which seemed to surprise her."

"It surprised me."

"But, surely, it was very obvious. I was then much surprised and interested on glancing down to observe that, though the boots which she was wearing were not unlike each other, they were really odd ones, the one having a slightly decorated toe-cap, and the other a plain one. One was buttoned only in the two lower buttons out of five, and the other at the first, third, and fifth. Now, when you see that a young lady, otherwise neatly dressed, has come away from home with odd boots, half buttoned, it is no great deduction to say that she came away in a hurry."

"And what else?" I asked, keenly interested, as I always was, by my friend's incisive reasoning.

"I noted, in passing, that she had written a note before leaving home, but after being fully dressed. You observed that her right glove was torn at the forefinger, but you did

24

fairly well to do: somewhat rich.   **easy-going**: unpretentious.

chuckled: laughed quietly.
'Pon my word: upon my word; believe me.   **coming along**: advancing; developing.
missed: failed to notice.
hit upon: found.
trust to: depend on.
details: particulars.   **glance**: look.
perhaps: maybe.

plush: fabric softer than velvet.   **most**: very.

of the hand type: powered by hand.
farthest: most distant.
broadest: widest.   **glanced**: looked.
dint: indentation.   **a pince-nez**: glasses held in place by a clip over the nose.   **ventured**: put forward.   **remark**: observation.
short sight: not being able to see far distances.

on glancing: on looking.
though: even if.   **unlike**: different.
odd: strange.
toe-cap: point.   **plain**: not decorated.

otherwise: in other respects.   **neatly**: carefully.
odd boots: strange boots.
in a hurry: very quickly.
keenly: very.
incisive: cutting; sharp.
noted: observed.
fully dressed: completely dressed.
torn: damaged.   **forefinger**: index finger.

not apparently see that both glove and finger were stained with violet ink. She had written in a hurry, and dipped her pen too deep. It must have been this morning, or the mark would not remain clear upon the finger. All this is amusing, though rather elementary, but I must go back to business, Watson. Would you mind reading me the advertised description of Mr. Hosmer Angel?"

I held the little printed slip to the light. "Missing," it said, on the morning of the 14th, a gentleman named Hosmer Angel. About 5ft. 7in. in height; strongly built, sallow complexion, black hair, a little bald in the centre, bushy black side whiskers and moustache; tinted glasses, slight infirmity of speech. Was dressed, when last seen, in black frock-coat faced with silk, black waistcoat, gold Albert chain, and grey Harris tweed trousers, with brown gaiters over elastic-sided boots. Known to have been employed in an office in Leadenhall Street. Anybody bringing," etc. etc.

"That will do," said Holmes. "As to the letters," he continued glancing over them, "they are very commonplace. Absolutely no clue in them to Mr. Angel, save that he quotes Balzac once. There is one remarkable point, however, which will no doubt strike you."

"They are typewritten," I remarked.

"Not only that, but the signature is typewritten. Look at the neat little 'Hosmer Angel' at the bottom. There is a date you see, but no superscription, except Leadenhall Street, which is rather vague. The point about the signature is very suggestive – in fact, we may call it conclusive."

"Of what?"

"My dear fellow, is it possible you do not see how strongly it bears upon the case."

"I cannot say that I do, unless it were that he wished to be able to deny his signature if an action for breach of promise were instituted."

"No, that was not the point. However, I shall write two letters which should settle the matter. One is to a firm in the City, the other is to the young lady's stepfather, Mr. Win-

stained: dirtied.

in a hurry: very quickly. **dipped**: put into the ink.

deep: deeply. **mark**: sign; spot.

upon: (archaic) on.

amusing: entertaining. **though**: even if.

business: work. **Would you mind reading**: would you be so kind as to read. **advertised**: published.

held: lifted; raised. **slip**: piece of paper. **Missing**: disappeared.

on the morning of the 14ᵗʰ: note the preposition *on*.

in height: tall.

sallow complexion: pale colour of the skin. **a little bald**: with little hair. **bushy**: thick. **side whiskers**: side beard. **tinted glasses**: dark glasses. **slight**: small. **last seen**: seen for the last time. **frock-coat**: long dress coat. **waistcoat**: sleeveless jacket. **gaiters**: coverings for shoes and ankles.

to have been employed: to have worked.

That will do: that's enough. **As to**: as concerns.

glancing: looking. **commonplace**: ordinary.

no clue: no key. **to Mr. Angel**: to find Mr. Angel. **save**: except.

quotes: repeats the words of. **once**: one time. **remarkable**: interesting. **however**: anyway. **strike**: impress.

remarked: observed.

signature: name.

neat: clean. **at the bottom**: at the bottom of the page.

superscription: address.

suggestive: significant.

fellow: man.

how strongly it bears upon: how important it is to.

it were: *subjunctive*.

to deny his signature: to say it was not his own signature. **action for breach**: legal action for breaking.

However: anyway.

should settle: should conclude. **matter**: affair. **firm**: company.

City: City of London, business area in central London.

dibank, asking him whether he could meet us here at six o'clock to-morrow evening. It is just as well that we should do business with the male relatives. And now, Doctor, we can do nothing until the answers to those letters come, so we may put our little problem upon the shelf for the interim.

I had had so many reasons to believe in my friend's subtle powers of reasoning, and extraordinary energy in action, that I felt that he must have some solid grounds for the assured and easy demeanour with which he treated the singular mystery which he had been called upon to fathom. Only once had I known him to fail, in the case of the King of Bohemia and of the Irene Adler photograph, but when I looked back to the weird business of the Sign of Four, and the extraordinary circumstances connected with the Study in Scarlet, I felt that it would be a strange tangle indeed which he could not unravel.

I left him then, still puffing at his black clay pipe, with the conviction that when I came again on the next evening I would find that he held in his hands all the clues which would lead up to the identity of the disappearing bridegroom of Miss Mary Sutherland.

A professional case of great gravity was engaging my own attention at the time, and the whole of next day I was busy at the bedside of the sufferer. It was not until close upon six o'clock that I found myself free, and was able to spring into a hansom and drive to Baker Street, half afraid that I might be too late to assist at the *dénouement* of the little mystery. I found Sherlock Holmes alone, however, half asleep, with his long, thin form curled up in the recesses of his armchair. A formidable array of bottles and test-tubes, with the pungent cleanly smell of hydrochloric acid, told me that he had spent his day in the chemical work which was so dear to him.

"Well, have you solved it?" I asked as I entered.

"Yes. It was the bisulphate of baryta."

"No, no, the mystery!" I cried.

"Oh, that! I thought of the salt that I have been working

whether: if.
just as well: better.
do business: treat the affair. **relatives**: members of the family.

interim: time between.
subtle: very clear.

grounds: reasons.
demeanour: manner.
called upon: asked. **fathom**: explain.
Only once had I known: note the *inversion*. **to fail**: not to succeed.
weird: strange. **Sign of Four**: Sherlock Holmes adventure.

Study in Scarlet: Sherlock Holmes adventure. **tangle**: intricate problem. **unravel**: solve.
puffing: smoking.
on the next evening: note the preposition *on*.
I would find: *future in the past*. **he held**: he had. **clues**: keys to the solution. **lead up**: take.
bridegroom: man about to be married.
gravity: seriousness. **engaging**: occupying.
the whole of next day: the entire next day.
close upon: almost.
spring: jump.
hansom: two-wheeled horse carriage.
dènouement: final revelation.
however: anyway.
form: body. **curled up**: rolled up. **recesses**: sides.
array: group. **test-tubes**: tubes for chemical experiments.

as: when.
baryta: barium oxide.
cried: shouted.

upon. There was never any mystery in the matter, though, as I said yesterday, some of the details are of interest. The only drawback is that there is no law, I fear, that can touch the scoundrel."

"Who was he, then, and what was his object in deserting Miss Sutherland?"

The question was hardly out of my mouth, and Holmes had not yet opened his lips to reply, when we heard a heavy footfall in the passage, and a tap at the door.

"This is the girl's stepfather, Mr. James Windibank," said Holmes. "He has written to me to say that he would be here at six. Come in!"

The man who entered was a sturdy middle-sized fellow, some thirty years of age, clean shaven, and sallow skinned, with a bland, insinuating manner, and a pair of wonderfully sharp and penetrating grey eyes. He shot a questioning glance at each of us, placed his shiny top-hat upon the sideboard, and, with a slight bow, sidled down into the nearest chair.

"Good evening, Mr. James Windibank," said Holmes. "I think that this typewritten letter is from you, in which you made an appointment with me for six o'clock!"

"Yes, sir. I am afraid that I am a little late, but I am not quite my own master, you know. I am sorry that Miss Sutherland has troubled you about this little matter, for I think it is far better not to wash linen of this sort in public. It was quite against my wishes that she came, but she is a very excitable, impulsive girl, as you may have noticed, and she is not easily controlled when she has made up her mind on a point. Of course, I do not mind you so much, as you are not connected with the official police, but it is not pleasant to have a family misfortune like this noised abroad. Besides, it is a useless expense, for how could you possibly find this Hosmer Angel?"

"On the contrary," said Holmes quietly; "I have every reason to believe that I will succeed in discovering Mr. Hosmer Angel."

Mr. Windibank gave a violent start, and dropped his

matter: affair. **though**: even if.
details: particulars.
drawback: problem.
scoundrel: bad man.
deserting: abandoning.

hardly: scarcely; barely.
to reply: to answer.
footfall: footstep. **passage**: hall. **a tap**: a knock.
stepfather: mother's second husband.
he would be here: *future in the past*.

sturdy: solid; strong.
fellow: man. **some**: about. **clean shaven**: with no beard.
sallow skinned: with a pale yellow skin. **bland**: dull; grey.
he shot: he threw; he cast.
questioning: interrogative. **glance**: look. **shiny**: glossy. **top-hat**: black cylindrical hat. **sideboard**: piece of furniture. **sidled down**: sat down.

is from you: comes from you.

I am afraid that I am: I am sorry for being.
I am not quite my own master: I am not in control of my own time.
matter: affair. **for**: because.
far better: much better. **to wash linen**: (idiom) to talk about private matters. **quite**: completely. **wishes**: desires.

she has made up her mind: she is convinced.
I do not mind you so much: you do not bother me so much.

misfortune: sad event. **noised abroad**: spread around.
Besides: in addition to this. **for**: because.

On the contrary: note the preposition *on*.
I will succeed in: I will have success in.

start: quick motion. **dropped**: let fall.

gloves.

"I am delighted to hear it," he said.

"It is a curious thing," remarked Holmes, "that a type-writer has really quite as much individuality as a man's handwriting. Unless they are quite new, no two of them write exactly alike. Some letters get more worn than others, and some wear only on one side. Now, you remark in this note of yours, Mr. Windibank, that in every case there is some little slurring over of the 'e', and a slight defect in the tail of the 'r'. There are fourteen other characteristics, but those are the more obvious."

"We do all our correspondence with this machine at the office, and no doubt it is a little worn," our visitor answered, glancing keenly at Holmes with his bright little eyes.

"And now I will show you what is really a very interesting study, Mr. Windibank," Holmes continued. "I think of writing another little monograph some of these days on the typewriter and its relation to crime. It is a subject to which I have devoted some little attention. I have here four letters which purport to come from the missing man. They are all typewritten. In each case, not only are the 'e's' slurred and the 'r's' tailless, but you will observe, if you care to use my magnifying lens, that the fourteen other characteristics to which I have alluded are there as well."

Mr. Windibank sprang out of his chair, and picked up his hat. "I cannot waste time over this sort of fantastic talk, Mr. Holmes," he said. "If you can catch the man, catch him, and let me know when you have done it."

"Certainly," said Holmes, stepping over and turning the key in the door. "I let you know, then, that I have caught him!"

"What! where?" shouted Mr. Windibank, turning white to his lips, and glancing about him like a rat in a trap.

"Oh, it won't do – really it won't," said Holmes suavely. "There is no possible getting out of it, Mr. Windibank. It is quite too transparent, and it was a very bad compliment when you said it was impossible for me to solve so simple

delighted: very pleased.
remarked: observed.

alike: in the same way. **worn**: deteriorated.
wear: deteriorate. **remark**: observe.
note: letter.
slurring: ink coming out. **slight**: small.

worn: deteriorated.
glancing: looking. **keenly**: sharply. **bright**: lively.

monograph: essay on a single subject.
subject: matter.
devoted: dedicated.
purport: claim; affirm. **missing**: disappeared.
slurred: stained.
tailless: without their tail. **if you care**: if you are so kind as.
magnifying lens: enlarging lens.
alluded: referred.
sprang: jumped.
fantastic: unbelievable.
catch: capture.

stepping over: crossing the room.
caught: captured.

shouted: cried. **turning**: becoming.
to his lips: even in his lips. **glancing about**: looking around.
won't do: will not work. **suavely**: smoothly.
getting out of it: way to escape from it.

impossible for me to solve: note the *infinitive construction*.

a question. That's right! Sit down, and let us talk it over."
Our visitor collapsed into a chair with a ghastly face and
a glitter of moisture on his brow. "It – it's not actionable,"
he stammered.

"I am very much afraid that it is not. But between
ourselves, Windibank, it was as cruel, and selfish, and
heartless a trick in a petty way as ever came before me.
Now, let me just run over the course of events, and you will
contradict me if I go wrong."

The man sat huddled up in his chair, with his head sunk
upon his breast, like one who is utterly crushed. Holmes
stuck his feet up on the corner of the mantelpiece, and
leaning back with his hands in his pockets, began talking,
rather to himself, as it seemed, than to us.

"The man married a woman very much older than himself
for her money," said he, "and he enjoyed the use of the
money of the daughter as long as she lived with them. It
was a considerable sum for people in their position, and the
loss of it would have made a serious difference. It was
worth an effort to preserve it. The daughter was of a good,
amiable disposition, but affectionate and warm-hearted in
her ways, so that it was evident that with her fair personal
advantages, and her little income, she would not be
allowed to remain single long. Now her marriage would
mean, of course, the loss of a hundred a year, so what does
her stepfather do to prevent it? He takes the obvious course
of keeping her at home, and forbidding her to seek the
company of people of her own age. But soon he found that
that would not answer for ever. She became restive,
insisted upon her rights, and finally announced her
positive intention of going to a certain ball. What does her
clever stepfather do then? He conceives an idea more
creditable to his head than to his heart. With the
connivance and assistance of his wife he disguised himself, covered those keen eyes with tinted glasses, masked
the face with a moustache and a pair of bushy whiskers,
sunk that clear voice into an insinuating whisper, and,
doubly secure on account of the girl's short sight, he

let us: *imperative.*   **talk it over**: discuss it.

collapsed: fell.   **ghastly**: deathly pale.

glitter: bit.   **moisture**: sweat; perspiration.   **brow**: forehead.   **actionable**: illegal.   **stammered**: stuttered; said hesitantly.

selfish: self-benefitting.

petty: mean.   **before me**: in front of me.

run over: examine quickly.

I go wrong: I make mistakes.

huddled up: with arms and legs close to his body.

utterly crushed: completely destroyed.

mantelpiece: shelf over the fireplace.

leaning back: reclining back.

rather: more.

as long as: for the time.

the loss of it: not having it any longer.

It was worth: it deserved.   **effort**: attempt.   **preserve**: keep.

amiable: friendly.   **disposition**: character.

income: money.

would not be allowed to: could not.   **single**: unmarried.

stepfather: mother's second husband.   **prevent**: avoid.   **course**: action.   **to seek**: to look for.

he found: he understood.

not answer: not be sufficient.   **restive**: restless; nervous.

upon: (archaic) on.

positive: serious.   **ball**: dance.

clever: intelligent; smart.   **stepfather**: mother's second husband.

conceives: forms.   **creditable**: of an honour.   **head**: mind.

connivance: assent.

disguised himself: hid his identity.   **keen**: sharp.   **tinted glasses**: dark glasses.   **a moustache**: note that *moustache* is singular.   **bushy**: thick.   **whiskers**: side beard.

doubly: much more.   **on account of**: because of.

appears as Mr. Hosmer Angel, and keeps off other lovers by making love himself"

"It was only a joke at first," groaned our visitor. "We never thought that she would have been so carried away."

"Very likely not. However that may be, the young lady was very decidedly carried away, and having quite made up her mind that her stepfather was in France, the suspicion of treachery never for an instant entered her mind. She was flattered by the gentleman's attentions, and the effect was increased by the loudly expressed admiration of her mother. Then Mr. Angel began to call, for it was obvious that the matter should be pushed as far as it would go, if a real effect were to be produced. There were meetings, and an engagement, which would finally secure the girl's affections from turning towards anyone else. But the deception could not be kept up for ever. These pretended journeys to France were rather cumbrous. The thing to do was clearly to bring the business to an end in such a dramatic manner that it would leave a permanent impression upon the young lady's mind, and prevent her from looking upon any other suitor for some time to come. Hence those vows of fidelity exacted upon a Testament, and hence also the allusions to a possibility of something happening on the very morning of the wedding. James Windibank wished Miss Sutherland to be so bound to Hosmer Angel, and so uncertain as to his fate, that for ten years to come, at any rate, she would not listen to another man. As far as the church door he brought her, and then, as he could go no further, he conveniently vanished away by the old trick of stepping in at one door of a four-wheeler, and out at the other. I think that that was the chain of events, Mr. Windibank!"

Our visitor had recovered something of his assurance while Holmes had been talking, and he rose from his chair now with a cold sneer upon his pale face.

"It may be so, or it may not, Mr. Holmes," said he, "but if you are so very sharp you ought to be sharp enough to know that it is you who are breaking the law now, and not

keeps off: keeps away.

groaned: said distressedly.
carried away: involved.
likely: probably.

having quite made up her mind: being quite convinced.
treachery: evil doing. **entered her mind**: note the *direct object* with *to enter*. **was flattered**: felt complimented.
increased: made greater.
for: because.
should be pushed: should be carried.
were to be produced: should be produced.
engagement: promise of marriage.
deception: trick.
be kept up: be continued. **pretended**: faked; false.
cumbrous: difficult to carry on; burdensome.

prevent her from looking: not allow her to look.
suitor: potential husband. **to come**: in the future. **Hence**: for which reason. **vows**: promises. **exacted**: asked.
on the very morning: on the same morning. Note the preposition *on*. **wished**: desired.
so bound to: so tied to.
fate: destiny. **to come**: in the future.
at any rate: at least.

vanished away: disappeared. **by**: by means of.
stepping in: entering. **four-wheeler**: horse carriage with four wheels. **chain**: sequence.

had recovered: had regained. **assurance**: self-control.
rose: stood up.
sneer: expression of scorn.

sharp: clever. **ought to**: should.

me. I have done nothing actionable from the first, but as long as you keep that door locked you lay yourself open to an action for assault and illegal constraint."

"The law cannot, as you say, touch you," said Holmes, unlocking and throwing open the door, "yet there never was a man who deserved punishment more. If the young lady has a brother or a friend he ought to lay a whip across your shoulders. By Jove!" he continued, flushing up at the sight of the bitter sneer upon the man's face, "it is not part of my duties to my client, but here's a hunting-crop handy, and I think I shall just treat myself to –" He took two swift steps to the whip, but before he could grasp it there was a wild clatter of steps upon the stairs, the heavy hall door banged, and from the window we could see Mr. James Windibank running at the top of his speed down the road. "There's a cold-blooded scoundrel!" said Holmes, laughing, as he threw himself down into his chair once more. "That fellow will rise from crime to crime until he does something very bad, and ends on a gallows. The case has, in some respects, been not entirely devoid of interest."

"I cannot now entirely see all the steps of your reasoning," I remarked.

"Well, of course it was obvious from the first that this Mr. Hosmer Angel must have some strong object for his curious conduct, and it was equally clear that the only man who really profited by the incident, as far as we could see, was the stepfather. Then the fact that the two men were never together, but that the one always appeared when the other was away, was suggestive. So were the tinted spectacles and the curious voice, which both hinted at a disguise, as did the bushy whiskers. My suspicions were all confirmed by his peculiar action in typewriting his signature, which of course inferred that his handwriting was so familiar to her that she would recognize even the smallest sample of it. You see all these isolated facts, together with many minor ones, all pointed in the same direction."

"And how did you verify them?"

actionable: illegal. **from the first**: from the beginning.
locked: closed. **you lay yourself open**: you expose yourself.
action: legal action.

unlocking: turning the key.
there never was a man: note the *inversion*. **deserved**: was owed. **he ought to**: he should.
lay a whip across your shoulders: strike your shoulders with a whip. **flushing up**: getting red. **sneer**: expression of scorn.
hunting-crop: small whip for horses. **handy**: near; at hand.
treat myself to: give myself the pleasure of.
grasp: take.
wild clatter: loud noise. **upon**: (archaic) on.
banged: closed with a loud noise.
at the top of his speed: as fast as he could.
cold-blooded: uncompassionate. **scoundrel**: bad man.

once more: again
gallows: structure on which men are executed by hanging.
devoid of: empty of; lacking.
steps: procedures.
remarked: observed.
from the first: from the beginning.
object: purpose.
curious: strange. **conduct**: behaviour.
profited: took advantages.
stepfather: mother's second husband.

suggestive: significant.
tinted spectacles: dark glasses. **hinted at**: suggested.
disguise: false identity. **bushy**: thick. **whiskers**: side beard.
peculiar: unusual; strange.
signature: name. **inferred**: let believe.

sample: part.

"Having once spotted my man, it was easy to get corroboration. I knew the firm for which this man worked. Having taken the printed description, I eliminated everything from it which could be the result of a disguise – the whiskers, the glasses, the voice, and I sent it to the firm, with a request that they would inform me whether it answered the description of any of their travellers. I had already noticed the peculiarities of the typewriter, and I wrote to the man himself at his business address, asking him if he would come here. As I expected, his reply was typewritten, and revealed the same trivial but characteristic defects. The same post brought me a letter from Westhouse & Marbank, of Fenchurch Street, to say that the description tallied in every respect with that of their employé, James Windibank. *Voilà tout!* "

"And Miss Sutherland?"

"If I tell her she will not believe me. You may remember the old Persian saying, 'There is danger for him who taketh the tiger cub, and danger also for whoso snatches a delusion from a woman.' There is as much sense in Hafiz as in Horace, and as much knowledge of the world."

COMPREHENSION QUESTIONS

1) Explain what Holmes means when he says that there is nothing so unnatural as the commonplace?

2) What was the husband's "cruelty" in the Dundas separation case?

3) Why does Holmes find smaller crimes more interesting than bigger crimes?

4) Describe Miss Mary Sutherland.

5) What does she want Holmes to do?

6) Why did Miss Sutherland's stepfather sell her father's business?

7) What does Miss Sutherland do with her own income?

8) Does her stepfather want her to go out?

9) What reason did Mr. Hosmer Angel give for not coming to her house when her stepfather was at home?

spotted: found.
corroboration: confirmation. **firm**: company.

disguise: false identity. **whiskers**: side beard.

they would inform: *future in the past*.
answered the description: corresponded to the description.
travellers: agents. **peculiarities**: characteristics.
himself: personally. **business address**: address at work.
reply: answer.
trivial: of little importance.
post: mail.

tallied: corresponded. **employé**: (archaic) employee.
Voilà tout: that's it.

taketh: takes.
the tiger cub: the baby tiger. **whoso**: who. **snatches**: takes
away.

---

10) What was Mr. Hosmer Angel like?
11) What did he make Miss Sutherland swear?
12) What happened on the wedding day?
13) What does Miss Sutherland think may have happened to Mr. Hosmer Angel?
14) What does Holmes advise Miss Sutherland to do?
15) What kind of details does Watson notice about Miss Sutherland's appearance?
16) How does Holmes know that Miss Sutherland types?
17) How does he know she left the house in a hurry that morning?
18) Describe Mr. James Windibank.
19) How does Holmes know that Mr. Hosmer Angel used the same typewriter as Mr. Windibank?
20) Why and how did Mr. Windibank pretend to be Mr. Hosmer Angel?

The Adventure of the
Sussex Vampire

Holmes had read carefully a note which the last post had brought him. Then, with the dry chuckle which was his nearest approach to a laugh, he tossed it over to me.

"For a mixture of the modern and the mediaeval, of the practical and of the wildly fanciful, I think this is surely the limit", said he.

"What do you make of it, Watson?"

I read as follows:

46, Old Jewry,
Nov. 19th

Re Vampires

Sir:

Our client, Mr. Robert Ferguson, of Ferguson and Muirhead, tea brokers, of Mincing Lane, has made some inquiry from us in a communication of even date concerning vampires. As our firm specializes entirely upon the assessment of machinery the matter hardly

carefully: with great attention. **note**: letter. **post**: mail.
dry chuckle: quiet laugh.
his nearest approach: as near as he ever got. **tossed**: threw.

wildly fanciful: most imaginative. **surely**: certainly.

do you make of it: do you think of it.

Re: reference; content of the letter.

tea brokers: importers of tea.
has made some inquiry from us: has asked us. *even date*: this
same date. *concerning*: about.
assessment: evaluation.

comes within our purview, and we have therefore re-
commended Mr. Ferguson to call upon you and lay
the matter before you. We have not forgotten your
successful action in the case of Matilda Briggs.
We are, sir,

Faithfully yours,
MORRISON, MORRISON, AND DODD.
per E. J. C.

"Matilda Briggs was not the name of a young woman, Watson", said Holmes in a reminiscent voice. "It was a ship which is associated with the giant rat of Sumatra, a story for which the world is not yet prepared. But what do we know about vampires? Does it come within our purview either? Anything is better than stagnation, but really we seem to have been switched on to a Grimms' fairy tale. Make a long arm, Watson, and see what V has to say".

I leaned back and took down the great index volume to which he referred. Holmes balanced it on his knee, and his eyes moved slowly and lovingly over the record of old cases, mixed with the accumulated information of a lifetime.

"Voyage of the *Gloria Scott* ", he read. "That was a bad business. I have some recollection that you made a record of it, Watson, though I was unable to congratulate you upon the result. Victor Lynch, the forger. Venomous lizard or gila. Remarkable case that! Vittoria, the circus belle Vanderbilt and the Yeggman. Vipers. Vigor, the Hammersmith wonder. Hullo! Hullo! Good old index. You can't beat it. Listen to this, Watson. Vampirism in Hungary. And again, Vampires in Transylvania". He turned over the pages with eagerness, but after a short intent perusal he threw down the great book with a snarl of disappointment. "Rubbish, Watson, rubbish! What have we to do with walking corpses who can only be held in their grave by stakes driven through their hears? It's pure lunacy".

"But surely ", said I, "the vampire was not necessarily a

hardly comes: does not even come. *purview*: reach; competence. *to call upon you*: to visit you.
lay the matter before you: present the problem to you.

reminiscent: remembering.
giant: very big.

purview: reach; competence. **stagnation**: inactivity.
to have been switched on to: to have entered.
fairy tale: fantastic story. **Make a long arm**: extend your arm.

leaned back: moved backwards. **index volume**: alphabetical listing of cases. **balanced**: placed.
lovingly: with affection. **record**: registration.

Voyage: journey.
business: affair. **recollection**: remembrance.

to congratulate you upon: note the preposition *upon* or *on*.
forger: maker of false banknotes. **gila**: big desert lizard. **circus belle**: beautiful woman of the circus. **Yeggman**: criminal.
wonder: marvellous man. **Hullo**: exclamation of satisfaction.
Listen to: note the preposition *to*.

eagerness: excitement. **intent**: very attentive. **perusal**: inspection. **snarl**: growl; exclamation. **disappointment**: dissatisfaction. **Rubbish**: nonsense.
corpses: bodies of dead men; cadavers. **be held**: be kept.
grave: tomb. **stakes**: wooden sticks. **driven**: hammered; impaled. **lunacy**: madness. **surely**: certainly.

dead man? A living person might have the habit. I have read, for example, of the old sucking the blood of the young in order to retain their youth".

"You are right, Watson. It mentions the legend in one of these references. But are we to give serious attention to such things? This agency stands flat-footed upon the ground, and there it must remain. The world is big enough for us. No ghosts need apply . I fear that we cannot take Mr. Robert Ferguson very seriously. Possibly this note may be from him and may throw some light upon what is worrying him".

He took up a second letter which had lain unnoticed upon the table while he had been absorbed with the first. This he began to read with a smile of amusement upon his face which gradually faded away into an expression of intense interest and concentration. When he had finished he sat for some little time lost in thought with the letter dangling from his fingers. Finally, with a start, he aroused himself from his reverie.

"Cheeseman's, Lamberley. Where is Lamberley, Watson?"

"It is in Sussex, south of Horsham".

"Not very far, eh? And Cheeseman's?"

"I know that country, Holmes. It is full of old houses which are named after the men who built them centuries ago. You get Odley's and Harvey's and Carriton's – the folk are forgotten but their names live in their houses.

"Precisely", said Holmes coldly. It was one of the peculiarities of his proud, self-contained nature that though he docketed any fresh information very quietly and accurately in his brain, he seldom made any acknowledgment to the giver. "I rather fancy we shall know a good deal more about Cheeseman's, Lamberley, before we are through. The letter is, as I had hoped, from Robert Ferguson. By the way, he claims acquaintance with you.

"With me!"

"You had better read it".

He handed the letter across. It was headed with the address

the old: old people.
the young: young people. **retain**: regain.

references: listings in the index. **are we to**: should we.
agency: detective business.
stands flat-footed upon the ground: is soundly anchored to reality. **ghosts**: spirits. **need apply**: have to come to us. **I fear**: I am afraid. **note**: letter.
throw some light upon: explain.

had lain: had been. **unnoticed**: unseen.
absorbed with: concentrating on.
amusement: fun; enjoyment.
faded away: disappeared.

dangling: being held loosely.
start: sudden movement.
reverie: state of deconcentration.

country: territory.
are named after: take the name of. **centuries**: hundreds of years. **the folk**: the people.

Precisely: exactly.
peculiarities: unique characteristics. **proud**: self-esteeming.
self-contained: kept within himself. **docketed**: recorded.
brain: mind. **seldom**: rarely.
made any acknowledgment: made any reference of having done so. **fancy**: believe. **a good deal**: much.
are through: have finished.
By the way: incidentally. **claims acquaintance with you**: says he knows you.
you had better: you should.
handed: passed. **was headed with**: had at the top of the paper.

quoted.
Dear Mr. Holmes [it said]:

> I have been recommended to you by my lawyers, but indeed the matter is so extraordinarily delicate that it is most difficult to discuss. It concerns a friend for whom I am acting. This gentleman married some five years ago a Peruvian lady, the daughter of a Peruvian merchant, whom he had met in connection with the importation of nitrates. The lady was very beautiful, but the fact of her foreign birth and of her alien religion always caused a separation of interests and of feelings between husband and wife, so that after a time his love may have cooled towards her and he may have come to regard their union as a mistake. He felt there were sides of her character which he could never explore or understand. This was the more painful as she was as loving a wife as a man could have – to all appearance absolutely devoted.

Now for the point which I will make more plain when we meet. Indeed, this note is merely to give you a general idea of the situation and to ascertain whether you would care to interest yourself in the matter. The lady began to show some curious traits quite alien to her ordinarily sweet and gentle disposition. The gentleman had been married twice and he had one son by the first wife. This boy was now fifteen, a very charming and affectionate youth, though unhappily injured through an accident in childhood. Twice the wife was caught in the act of assaulting this poor lad in the most unprovoked way. Once she struck him with a stick and left a great weal on his arm.

This was a small matter, however, compared with her conduct to her own child, a dear boy just under one year of age. On one occasion about a month ago this child had been left by its nurse for a few minutes. A loud cry from the baby, as of pain, called the nurse back. As she ran into the room she saw her employer, the lady,

quoted: already mentioned.

lawyers: legal advisers.

most: very. **it concerns**: it is about.
for whom I am acting: whom I am representing. **some**: about.

in connection with: as a consequence to.

alien: different; foreign.

after a time: after some time.
cooled: got colder.
to regard: to consider. **sides**: aspects.

painful: sorrowful.
loving: affectionate. **to all appearance**: from all visible signs.

plain: clear.
note: letter. **merely**: simply.
ascertain: find out. **whether**: if.
would care: would like. **matter**: affair.
curious: strange. **traits**: characteristics. **alien to**: different from.
ordinarily: usually. **disposition**: temperament.

charming: pleasant.
youth: young man. **injured**: damaged.
in childhood: happened when he was a child.
caught: surprised. **lad**: boy.
in the most unprovoked way: without any reason at all. **struck**:
beat. **weal**: bruise.
small: insignificant.
conduct: behaviour. **her own**: *own* intensifies the possessive.
On one occasion: note the preposition *on*.
its nurse: the woman who took care of it. Note that *child* is
considered *neuter*. **pain**: sufferance.
her employer: the woman she worked for.

*leaning over the baby and apparently biting his neck.
There was a small wound in the neck from which a
stream of blood had escaped. The nurse was so horri-
fied that she wished to call the husband, but the lady
implored her not to do so and actually gave her five
pounds as a price for her silence. No explanation was
ever given, and for the moment the matter was passed
over.*

*It left, however, a terrible impression upon the nurse's
mind, and from that time she began to watch her
mistress closely and to keep a closer guard upon the
baby, whom she tenderly loved. It seemed to her that
even as she watched the mother, so the mother watched
her, and that every time she was compelled to leave the
baby alone the mother was waiting to get at it. Day and
night the nurse covered the child, and day and night the
silent, watchful mother seemed to be lying in wait as a
wolf waits for a lamb. It must read most incredible to
you, and yet I beg you to take it seriously, for a child's
life and a man's sanity may depend upon it.*

*At last there came one dreadful day when the facts
could no longer be concealed from the husband. The
nurse's nerve had given way; she could stand the strain
no longer, and she made a clean breast of it all to the
man. To him it seemed as wild a tale as it may now seem
to you. He knew his wife to be a loving wife, and, save
for the assaults upon her stepson, a loving mother.
Why, then, should she wound her own dear little baby?
He told the nurse that she was dreaming, that her suspicions were those of a lunatic, and that such libels upon
her mistress were not to be tolerated. While they were
talking a sudden cry of pain was heard. Nurse and
master rushed together to the nursery. Imagine his
feelings, Mr. Holmes, as he saw his wife rise from a
kneeling position beside the cot and saw blood upon the
child's exposed neck and upon the sheet. With a cry of
horror, he turned his wife's face to the light and saw
blood all round her lips. It was she – she beyond all*

leaning: curved.

stream: flow.   *escaped*: come out.
wished: wanted.
actually: as a matter of fact.

the matter: the affair.
was passed over: was overlooked.
however: anyway.   *upon*: (archaic) on.
to watch: observe.
mistress: lady.   *closely*: carefully.   *closer*: more attentive; more careful.   *tenderly*: sweetly.

she was compelled: she was forced; she was obliged.
to get at it: to reach it.
covered the child: protected the child.
watchful: vigilant; alert.   *to be lying in wait*: to be waiting.
read: seem; appear.   *most*: very.
I beg: I implore.   *for*: because.
sanity: mental health.   *upon*: on.
At last: in the end.   *dreadful*: horrible.
concealed: hidden; kept secret.
had given way: had broken down.   *strain*: stress.
she made a clean breast: (idiom) she confessed everything.
wild: crazy; unbelievable.
He knew his wife to be: note the *infinitive construction*.   *loving*: affectionate.   *save*: except.   *stepson*: son of the husband from his first wife.   *wound*: harm.

lunatic: crazy woman.   *libels*: false accusations.
mistress: lady.
sudden: unexpected.   *pain*: suffering.
rushed: ran.   *nursery*: baby's room.
as: when.   *rise*: stand up.
a kneeling position: down on her knees.   *beside*: next to.   *cot*: small bed.

question – who had drunk the poor baby's blood.
So the matter stands. She is now confined to her room.
There has been no explanation. The husband is half
demented. He knows, and I know, little of vampirism
beyond the name. We had thought it was some wild tale
of foreign parts. And yet here in the very heart of the
English Sussex – well, all this can be discussed with you
in the morning. Will you see me? Will you use your
great powers in aiding a distracted man? If so, kindly
wire to Ferguson, Cheeseman's, Lamberley, and I will
be at your rooms by ten o'clock.

Yours faithfully,
ROBERT FERGUSON.

P. S. I believe your friend Watson played Rugby for
Blackheath when I was three-quarter for Richmond. It
is the only personal introduction which I can give.

"Of course I remembered him", said I as I laid down the letter. "Big Bob Ferguson, the finest three-quarter Richmond ever had. He was always a good-natured chap. It's like him to be so concerned over a friend's case".

Holmes looked at me thoughtfully and shook his head.

"I never get your limits, Watson", said he. "There are unexplored possibilities about you. Take a wire down, like a good fellow. 'Will examine your case with pleasure'".

"Your case!"

"We must not let him think that this agency is a home for the weak-minded. Of course it is his case. Send him that wire and let the matter rest till morning.

Promptly at ten o'clock next morning Ferguson strode into our room. I had rememberded him as a long, slabsided man with loose limbs and a fine turn of speed which had carried him round many an opposing back. There is surely nothing in life more painful than to meet the wreck of a fine athlete whom one has known in his prime. His great frame had fallen in, his flaxen hair was scanty, and his shoulders were bowed. I fear that I roused corresponding emotions in him.

beyond all question: with no doubt.
So the matter stands: this is where the affair is now.

half demented: almost mad.
beyond: except. *wild*: unbelievable. *tale*: story.
in the very heart: in the centre.

aiding: helping. *distracted*: desperate. *If so*: if you agree.
wire: send a telegram.
at your rooms: at your flat. *by*: not later than.

believe: think.
three-quarter: player in the defense line.
introduction: reference.

Of course: certainly. **I laid**: I put.
the finest: the best.
good-natured: cheerful. **chap**: man.
It's like him: it is typical of him. **concerned**: worried.
shook his head: moved his head side to side to show disapproval. **I never get your limits**: your limits are always a surprise to me. **Take a wire down**: write a telegram.
fellow: man.

the weak-minded: stupid people.
wire: telegram. **matter**: affair. **rest**: be forgotten.
Promptly: exactly. **strode**: walked.
slabsided: slim.
loose: agile. **limbs**: arms and legs. **fine**: good.
many an opposing back: the back of many opponents.
painful: sorrowful. **wreck**: ruin. **fine**: good.
in his prime: in his best days. **frame**: body.
fallen in: fallen apart; decayed. **flaxen**: blond. **scanty**: mostly gone. **bowed**: curved. **roused**: caused.

"Hullo, Watson", said he, and his voice was still deep and hearty. "You don't look quite the man you did when I threw you over the ropes into the crowd at the Old Deer Park. I expect I have changed a bit also. But it's this last day or two that has aged me. I see by your telegram, Mr. Holmes, that it is no use my pretending to be anyone's deputy.

"It is simpler to deal direct", said Holmes.

"Of course it is. But you can imagine how difficult it is when you are speaking of the one woman whom you are bound to protect and help. What can I do? How am I to go to the police with such a story? And yet the kiddies have got to be protected. Is it madness, Mr. Holmes? Is it something in the blood? Have you any similar case in your experience? For God's sake, give me some advice, for I am at my wit's end".

"Very naturally, Mr. Ferguson. Now sit here and pull yourself together and give me a few clear answers. I can assure you that I am very far from being at my wit's end, and that I am confident we shall find some solution. First of all, tell me what steps you have taken. Is your wife still near the children?"

"We had a dreadful scene. She is a most loving woman, Mr. Holmes. If ever a woman loved a man with all her heart and soul, she loves me. She was cut to the heart that I should have discovered this horrible, this incredible, secret. She would not even speak. She gave no answer to my reproaches, save to gaze at me with a sort of wild, despairing look in her eyes. Then she rushed to her room and locked herself in. Since then she has refused to see me. She has a maid who was with her before her marriage, Dolores by name – a friend rather than a servant. She takes her food to her".

"Then the child is in no immediate danger?"

"Mrs. Mason, the nurse, has sworn that she will not leave it night or day. I can absolutely trust her. I am more uneasy about poor little Jack, for, as I told you in my note, he has twice been assaulted by her".

hearty: strong.
crowd: spectators.

has aged me: has caused me to get older.
pretending: acting.
deputy: representative.
to deal: to have to do. **direct**: directly.
Of course: certainly.

you are bound: you promised.
such a story: a story like this. **kiddies**: children.

For God's sake: exclamation of impatience. **advice**: counsel.
for: because. **I am at my wit's end**: I am close to madness.

pull yourself together: regain your composure.

I am confident: I am sure.
steps: moves; actions.

dreadful: horrible. **most loving**: very affectionate.

cut to the heart: hurt deeply.

reproaches: criticisms. **save**: except. **gaze**: look. **a sort**: a kind.
wild: crazy. **look**: expression. **rushed**: ran.
locked: closed.
maid: girl servant.
Dolores by name: her name is Dolores.

immediate: present.
nurse: woman who takes care of the child. **sworn**: promised
solemnly. **trust**: be sure of. **uneasy**: worried.
note: letter.
twice: two times.

"But never wounded?"

"No, she struck him savagely. It is the more terrible as he is a poor little inoffensive cripple. Ferguson's gaunt features softened as he spoke of his boy. "You would think that the dear lad's condition would soften anyone's heart. A fall in childhood and a twisted spine, Mr. Holmes. But the dearest, most loving heart within".

Holmes had picked up the letter of yesterday and was reading it over. "What other inmates are there in your house, Mr. Ferguson?"

"Two servants who have not been long with us. One stablehand, Michael, who sleeps in the house. My wife, myself, my boy Jack, baby, Dolores, and Mrs. Mason. That is all".

"I gather that you did not know your wife well at the time of your marriage?"

"I had only known her a few weeks".

"How long had this maid Dolores been with her?"

"Some years".

"Then your wife's character would really be better known by Dolores than by you?"

"Yes, you may say so".

Holmes made a note.

"I fancy", said he, "that I may be of more use at Lamberley than here. It is eminently a case for personal investigation. If the lady remains in her room, our presence could not annoy or inconvenience her. Of course, we would stay at the inn".

Ferguson gave a gesture of relief.

"It is what I hoped, Mr. Holmes. There is an excellent train at two from Victoria if you could come".

"Of course we could come. There is a lull at present. I can give you my undivided energies. Watson, of course, comes with us. But there are one or two points upon which I wish to be very sure before I start. This unhappy lady, as I understand it, has appeared to assault both the children, her own baby and your little son?"

"That is so".

wounded: hurt.
struck: beat.   **savagely**: wildly.
cripple: disabled person.   **gaunt**: tight.
features: face.   **softened**: became less rigid.
lad's: boy's.
in childhood: when he was a child.   **twisted spine**: bent backbone.   **loving**: affectionate.   **within**: inside him.

reading it over: reading it again.   **inmates**: cohabitors.

have not been long: *duration form*.   **long**: for a long time.
stablehand: groom.

I gather: I understand.

I had only known her a few weeks: *duration form*.   **a few weeks**:
for a few weeks.   **maid**: servant.

you may say so: *may* expresses *possibility*.
made a note: wrote something down.
I fancy: I believe.   **of more use**: more useful.

annoy: bother.   **inconvenience**: disturb.
inn: small hotel.
relief: relaxation.

Victoria: main station in London.
lull: period of inactivity.   **at present**: now.
undivided: complete; entire.
upon: (archaic) on.   **I wish**: I desire.

her own baby: *own* intensifies the possessive.
That is so: correct.

"But the assaults take different forms, do they not? She has beaten your son".

"Once with a stick and once very savagely with her hands".

"Did she give no explanation why she struck him?"

"None save that she hated him. Again and again she said so".

"Well, that is not unknown among stepmothers. A posthumous jealousy, we will say. Is the lady jealous by nature?"

"Yes, she is very jealous – jealous with all the strength of her fiery tropical love".

"But the boy – he is fifteen, I understand, and probably very developed in mind, since his body has been circumscribed in action. Did he give you no explanation of these assaults?"

"No, he declared there was no reason".

"Were they good friends at other times?"

"No, there was never any love between them".

"Yet you say he is affectionate?"

" Never in the world could there be so devoted a son. My life is his life. He is absorbed in what I say or do".

Once again Holmes made a note. For some time he sat lost in thought.

"No doubt you and the boy were great comrades before this second marriage. You were thrown very close together, were you not?"

"Very much so".

"And the boy, having so affectionate a nature, was devoted, no doubt, to the memory of his mother?"

"Most devoted".

"He would certainly seem to be a most interesting lad. There is one other point about these assaults. Were the strange attacks upon the baby and the assaults upon your son at the same period?"

"In the first case it was. It was as if some frenzy had seized her, and she had vented her rage upon both. In the second case it was only Jack who suffered. Mrs. Mason had no complaint to make about the baby".

"That certainly complicates matters".

do they not?: *question-tag*.

stick: piece of wood.   **savagely**: wildly.
she struck: she beat.
save: except.   **Again and again**: repeatedly.

unknown: uncommon.   **stepmothers**: fathers 'second wives.
posthumous: after death.

fiery: hot.

developed in mind: intelligent.
circumscribed: disabled.

at other times: in other moments.

Never in the world could there be: note the *inversion*.
absorbed: deeply interested.
made a note: wrote something down.

comrades: friends.
close: near.
were you not?: *question-tag*.

devoted: loyal.
Most: very.
lad: boy.

upon: (archaic) on.

frenzy: extremely agitated and uncontrolled action.   **seized**:
possessed.   **had vented**: had expressed.   **rage**: fury.   **both**: the
two.

matters: the affair.

"I don't quite follow you, Mr. Holmes".

"Possibly not. One forms provisional theories and waits for time or fuller knowledge to explode them. A bad habit, Mr. Ferguson, but human nature is weak. I fear that your old friend has given an exaggerated view of my scientific methods. However, I will only say at the present stage that your problem does not appear to me to be insoluble, and that you may expect to find us at Victoria at two o'clock".

It was evening of a dull, foggy November day when, having left our bags at the Chequers, Lamberley, we drove through the Sussex clay of a long winding lane and finally reached the isolated and ancient farmhouse in which Ferguson dwelt. It was a large, straggling building, very old in the centre, very new at the wings with towering Tudor chimneys and a lichen-spotted, high-pitched roof. The doorsteps were worn into curves, and the ancient tiles which lined the porch were marked with the rebus of a cheese and a man after the original builder. Within, the ceilings were corrugated with heavy oaken beams, and the uneven floors sagged into sharp curves. An odour of age and decay pervaded the whole crumbling building.

There was one very large central room into which Ferguson led us. Here, in a huge old-fashioned fireplace with an iron screen behind it dated 1670, there blazed and spluttered a splendid log fire.

The room, as I gazed round, was a most singular mixture of dates and of places. The half-panelled walls may well have belonged to the original yeoman farmer of the seventeenth century. They were ornamented, however, on the lower part by a line of well-chosen modern water-colours; while above, where yellow plaster took the place of oak, there was hung a fine collection of South American utensils and weapons, which had been brought, no doubt, by the Peruvian lady upstairs. Holmes rose, with that quick curiosity which sprang from his eager mind, and examined them with some care. He returned with his eyes full of thought.

"Hullo!" he cried. "Hullo!".

provisional: temporary.
fuller: more. **explode**: destroy.
I fear: I am afraid.

stage: step of development.

Victoria: main station in London.
dull: grey.
bags: luggage. **Chequers**: name of the inn.
clay: soft earth. **winding**: with many curves. **lane**: small road.
farmhouse: country house.
dwelt: lived. **straggling**: expanded in an irregular way.
wings: sides. **towering**: very tall. **Tudor**: in Tudor style. (Tudor:
English royal house ruling from 1485 to 1603). **high-pitched**:
with steeply sloping sides. **worn**: deteriorated.
porch: entrance.
after: representing the name of. **Within**: inside.
oaken beams: horizontal pieces of wood. **uneven**: irregular.
sagged: sank.
whole: entire; complete. **crumbling**: falling apart.

led us: took us. **huge**: very large. **old-fashioned**: antique.
screen: panel. **blazed**: burned.
spluttered: exploded. **log fire**: fire produced by a large piece of
wood. **I gazed**: I looked. **most**: very.
The half-panelled walls: the walls with panels covering only half
of them. **have belonged**: have been the property of. **yeoman
farmer**: owner of the estate. **ornamented**: decorated. **however**: anyway. **water-colours**: paintings.
took the place of: substituted. **oak**: wood.

upstairs: who was on the upper floor. **rose**: stood up.
sprang: came out. **eager**: very curious.
care: attention.

A spaniel had lain in a basket in the corner. It came slowly forward towards its master, walking with difficulty. Its hind legs moved irregularly and its tail was on the ground. It licked Ferguson's hand.

"What is it, Mr. Holmes?"

"The dog. What's the matter with it?"

"That's what puzzled the vet. A sort of paralysis. Spinal meningitis, he thought. But it is passing. He'll be all right soon – won't you, Carlo?"

A shiver of assent passed through the drooping tail. The dog's mournful eyes passed from one of us to the other. He knew that we were discussing his case.

"Did it come on suddenly?"

"In a single night".

"How long ago?"

"It may have been four months ago".

"Very remarkable. Very suggestive".

"What do you see in it, Mr. Holmes?"

"A confirmation of what I had already thought".

"For God's sake, what *do* you think, Mr. Holmes? It may be a mere intellectual puzzle to you, but it is life and death to me! My wife a would-be murderer – my child in constant danger! Don't play with me, Mr. Holmes. It is too terribly serious".

The big Rugby three-quarter was trembling all over. Holmes put his hand soothingly upon his arm.

"I fear that there is pain for you, Mr. Ferguson, whatever the solution may be", said he. "I would spare you all I can. I cannot say more for the instant, but before I leave this house I hope I may have something definite".

"Please God you may! If you will excuse me, gentlemen, I will go up to my wife's room and see if there has been any change".

He was away some minutes, during which Holmes resumed his examination of the curiosities upon the wall. When our host returned it was clear from his downcast face that he had made no progress.

He brought with him a tall, slim, brown-faced girl.

spaniel: dog.

hind legs: back legs.

puzzled: perplexed. **vet**: veterinarian. **a sort**: a kind.
all right: recovered.
won't you?: *question-tag*.
shiver: sudden spasm. **assent**: agreement. **drooping**: hanging.
mournful: very sad.

come on: begin.

It may: *may* expresses possibilty.
remarkable: interesting. **suggestive**: significant.

For God's sake: exclamation of anxiety.
a mere: only an. **puzzle**: game.
a would-be: a probable. **murderer**: killer.

three-quarter: player in the defense line.
soothingly: compassionately.
pain: sorrow. **whatever**: it doesn't matter what.
spare you: protect you.

resumed: began again. **curiosities**: strange objects.
our host: the person who gave us hospitality. **downcast**: sad.
he had made no progress: the situation had not changed.
slim: thin; skinny.

"The tea is ready, Dolores ", said Ferguson. "See that your mistress has everything she can wish".

"She verra ill", cried the girl, looking with indignant eyes at her master. "She no ask for food. She verra ill. She need doctor. I frightened stay alone with her without doctor".

Ferguson looked at me with a question in his eyes.

"I should be so glad if I could be of use".

"Would your mistress see Dr. Watson?"

"I take him. I no ask leave. She needs doctor".

"Then I'll come with you at once".

I followed the girl, who was quivering with strong emotion, up the staircase and down an ancient corridor. At the end was an iron-clamped and massive door. It struck me as I looked at it that if Ferguson tried to force his way to his wife he would find it no easy matter. The girl drew a key from her pocket, and the heavy oaken planks creaked upon their old hinges. I passed in and she swiftly followed, fastening the door behind her.

On the bed a woman was lying who was clearly in a high fever. She was only half conscious, but as I entered she raised a pair of frightened but beautiful eyes and glared at me in apprehension. Seeing a stranger, she appeared to be relieved and sank back with a sigh upon the pillow. I stepped up to her with a few reassuring words, and she lay still while I took her pulse and temperature. Both were high, and yet my impression was that the condition was rather that of mental and nervous excitement than of any actual seizure.

"She lie like that one day, two day. I 'fraid she die", said the girl.

The woman turned her flushed and handsome face towards me.

"Where is my husband?"

"He is below and would wish to see you".

"I will not see him. I will not see him ". Then she seemed to wander off into delirium. "A fiend! A fiend! Oh, what shall I do with this devil

"Can I help you in any way?"

64

mistress: lady.   **wish**: desire.
verra: very.
no ask: does not ask.   **She need**: she needs.
doctor: a doctor.   **I frightened**: I am frightened; I am scared.
stay: to stay.
so glad: very pleased.   **of use**: useful.
mistress: lady.
I no ask: I will not ask.   **leave**: her permission.   **doctor**: a doctor.
at once: immediately.
quivering: trembling.

iron-clamped: sealed with iron hinges.   **massive**: very heavy.   **It struck me**: I noticed.   **to force his way**: to enter by force.

drew a key from: took a key out of.   **oaken**: wooden.   **planks**: boards.   **hinges**: pivots.   **passed in**: entered.
fastening: locking; closing.

was clearly in a high fever: evidently had high temperature.   **as**: when.   **raised**: lifted.   **glared**: looked.
in apprehension: very worried.
relieved: relaxed.   **sigh**: deep breath.   **pillow**: bed cushion.
stepped: walked.
still: motionless.

actual: real.   **seizure**: disease.
She lie: she has been lying.   **one day**: for one day.   **I 'fraid**: I am afraid.   **she die**: she dies.
flushed: red.   **handsome**: beautiful.

below: downstairs.   **would wish**: would like.

wander off: go away.   **fiend**: devil.

"No. No one can help: It is finished. All is destroyed. Do what I will, all is destroyed"

The woman must have some strange delusion. I could not see honest Bob Ferguson in the character of fiend or devil.

"Madame", I said, "your husband loves you dearly. He is deeply grieved at this happening".

Again she turned on me those glorious eyes.

"He loves me. Yes. But do I not love him? Do I not love him even to sacrifice myself rather than break his dear heart? That is how I love him. And yet he could think of me – he could speak of me so".

"He is full of grief but he cannot understand".

"No, he cannot understand. But he should trust".

"Will you not see him?" I suggested.

"No, no, I cannot forget those terrible words nor the look upon his face. I will not see him. Go now. You can do nothing for me. Tell him only one thing. I want my child. I have a right to my child. That is the only message I can send him". She turned her face to the wall and would say no more.

I returned to the room downstairs, where Ferguson and Holmes still sat by the fire. Ferguson listened moodily to my account of the interview.

"How can I send her the child?" he said. "How do I know what strange impulse might come upon her? How can I ever forget how she rose from beside it with its blood upon her lips?" He shuddered at the recollection "The child is safe with Mrs. Mason, and there he must remain".

A smart maid, the only modern thing which we had seen in the house, had brought in some tea. As she was serving it the door opened and a youth entered the room. He was a remarkable lad pale faced and fair-haired, with excitable light blue eyes which blazed into a sudden flame of emotion and joy as they rested upon his father. He rushed forward and threw his arms round his neck with the abandon of a loving girl.

"Oh, daddy", he cried, "I did not know that you were due yet". I should have been here to meet you. Oh, I am so glad

must have: *supposition in the past*. **delusion**: false impression of reality.
dearly: very much.
deeply: very. **grieved**: sad. **happening**: fact.
glorious: beautiful.

so: in the way he did.
grief: sorrow.
he should trust: he should believe in me.

look: expression.
upon: (archaic) on.

would say no more: refused to say more.

by: near. **moodily**: sadly.
account: narration. **interview**: conversation.

rose: stood up. **beside**: next to.
shuddered: trembled. **recollection**: remembrance.
safe: secure.
smart: fashionable. **maid**: girl servant.

youth: young man. **entered the room**: note the direct object with *to enter*. **remarkable**: exceptional. **lad**: boy. **fair-haired**: with blond hair. **light blue**: pale blue. **blazed into**: became lighted with. **as**: when. **rested**: stopped. **rushed**: ran.

were due yet: were expected now. **glad**: happy.

to see you!".

Ferguson gently disengaged himself from the embrace with some little show of embarrassment.

"Dear old chap", said he, patting the flaxen head with a very tender hand. "I came early because my friends, Mr. Holmes and Dr. Watson, have been persuaded to come down and spend an evening with us".

"Is that Mr. Holmes, the detective?"

"Yes".

The youth looked at us with a very penetrating and, as it seemed to me, unfriendly gaze.

"What about your other child, Mr Ferguson?" asked Holmes. "Might we make the acquaintance of the baby?"

"Ask Mrs. Mason to bring baby down" said Ferguson. The boy went off with a curious, shambling gait which told my surgical eyes that he was suffering from a weak spine. Presently he returned, and behind him came a tall, gaunt woman bearing in her arms a very beautiful child, dark-eyed, golden-haired, a wonderful mixture of the Saxon and the Latin. Ferguson was evidently devoted to it, for he took it into his arms and fondled it most tenderly.

"Fancy anyone having the heart to hurt him", he muttered as he glanced down at the small, angry red pucker upon the cherub throat.

It was at this moment that I chanced to glance at Holmes and saw a most singular intentness in his expression. His face was as set as if it had been carved out of old ivory, and his eyes, which had glanced for a moment at father and child, were now fixed with eager curiosity upon something at the other side of the room. Following his gaze I could only guess that he was looking out through the window at the melancholy, dripping garden. It is true that a shutter had half closed outside and obstructed the view, but none the less it was certainly at the window that Holmes was fixing his concentrated attention. Then he smiled, and his eyes came back to the baby. On its chubby neck there was this small puckered mark. Without speaking Holmes examined it with care. Finally he shook one of the dimpled

disengaged: freed.

show: expression.

chap: fellow; man. **patting**: beating affectionately. **flaxen**: blond. **tender**: delicate; soft. **came**: arrived.

persuaded: convinced.

youth: young man.

gaze: look.

make the acquaintance of: meet.

went off: went away. **shambling gait**: unsteady way of walking.

surgical: medically trained. **suffering from**: note the preposition *from*. **spine**: backbone. **Presently**: after a short time. **gaunt**: thin.

dark-eyed: with dark eyes. **golden-haired**: with blond hair.

was evidently devoted to: evidently loved. **for**: because.

fondled: cuddled. **most**: very.

Fancy: imagine. **heart**: lack of compassion. **muttered**: said in a low voice. **glanced**: looked. **angry red**: bright red. **pucker**: mark. **cherub**: baby angel.

chanced to glance: looked by chance.

a most singular: a very strange.

set: motionless. **carved**: cut.

glanced: looked.

eager: intense curiosity.

gaze: look.

guess: imagine.

melancholy: sad. **dripping**: wet. **shutter**: window door.

none the less: however; anyway.

chubby: fat.

puckered mark: wrinkled mark.

care: attention. **shook**: moved. **dimpled**: fat; indented.

fists which waved in front of him.

"Good-bye, little man. You have made a strange start in life. Nurse, I should wish to have a word with you in private".

He took her aside and spoke earnestly for a few minutes. I only heard the last words, which were: "Your anxiety will soon, I hope, be set at rest". The woman, who seemed to be a sour, silent kind of creature, withdrew with the child.

"What is Mrs. Mason like?" asked Holmes.

"Not very prepossessing externally, as you can see, but a heart of gold, and devoted to the child".

"Do you like her, Jack?" Holmes turned suddenly upon the boy. His expressive mobile face shadowed over, and he shook his head.

"Jacky has very strong likes and dislikes", said Ferguson, putting his arm round the boy. "Luckily I am one of his likes".

The boy cooed and nestled his head upon his father's breast. Ferguson gently disengaged him.

"Run away, little Jacky", said he, and he watched his son with loving eyes until he disappeared. "Now, Mr. Holmes", he continued when the boy was gone. "I really feel that I have brought you on a fool's errand, for what can you possibly do save give me your sympathy? It must be an exceedingly delicate and complex affair from your point of view".

"It is certainly delicate", said my friend with an amused smile, "but I have not been struck up to now with its complexity. It has been a case for intellectual deduction, but when this original intellectual deduction is confirmed point by point by quite a number of independent incidents, then the subjective becomes objective and we can say confidently that we have reached our goal. I had, in fact, reached it before we left Baker Street, and the rest has merely been observation and confirmation".

Ferguson put his big hand to his furrowed forehead.

"For heaven's sake. Holmes", he said hoarsely, "if you can see the truth in this matter, do not keep me in suspense.

fists: closed hands. **waved**: agitated.
start: beginning.
to have a word with you: to talk to you.

earnestly: seriously.

be set at rest: be calmed. **seemed to be**: appeared to be.
sour: unhappy. **withdrew**: left the room; exited.

prepossessing: attractive.
a heart of gold: very good. **devoted to**: very attached to.
turned suddenly upon: talked suddenly to.
shadowed over: became serious.
shook his head: moved his head as to say "no".
dislikes: disaffections.

cooed: made a sound showing his pleasure.
disengaged him: pulled him apart.

I have brought you on a fool's errand: I have made you waste
your time. **for**: because. **save**: except. **sympathy**: compassion.

amused: entertained.
up to now: until now.

confidently: with certainty. **goal**: purpose; aim.

merely: only.
furrowed: wrinkled.
For heaven's sake: exclamation of impatience. **hoarsely**: gra-
vily.

How do I stand? What shall I do? I care nothing as to how you have found your facts so long as you have really got them".

"Certainly I owe you an explanation, and you shall have it. But you will permit me to handle the matter in my own way? Is the lady capable of seeing us, Watson?"

"She is ill, but she is quite rational".

"Very good. It is only in her presence that we can clear the matter up. Let us go up to her".

"She will not see me", cried Ferguson.

"Oh, yes, she will ", said Holmes. He scribbled a few lines upon a sheet of paper. "You at least have the entrée, Watson. Will you have the goodness to give the lady this note?"

I ascended again and handed the note to Dolores, who cautiously opened the door. A minute later I heard a cry from within, a cry in which joy and surprise seemed to be blended. Dolores looked out.

"She will see them. She will leesten", said she.

At my summons Ferguson and Holmes came up. As we entered the room Ferguson took a step or two towards his wife, who had raised herself in the bed, but she held out her hand to repulse him. He sank into an armchair, while Holmes seated himself beside him after bowing to the lady, who looked at him with wide-eyed amazement.

"I think we can dispense with Dolores", said Holmes, "Oh, very well, madame, if you would rather she stayed I can see no objection. Now, Mr. Ferguson, I am a busy man with many calls, and my methods have to be short and direct. The swiftest surgery is the least painful. Let me first say what will ease your mind. Your wife is a very good, a very loving, and a very ill-used woman".

Ferguson sat up with a cry of joy.

"Prove that, Mr. Holmes, and I am your debtor forever".

"I will do so, but in doing so I must wound you deeply in another direction".

"I care nothing so long as you clear my wife. Everything on earth is insignificamt compared to that".

How do I stand?: what is my condition? **I care nothing as to how**: I am not intersted in how.

I owe you: I have to give you.
handle: treat. **matter**: affair. **own**: personal.
capable of seeing us: able to see us.

cried: shouted.
He scribbled: he wrote down quickly.
entrée: permission of entering.
Will you have the goodness: will you be so kind as.
note: written paper.
I ascended: I went upstairs. **handed the note**: gave the written paper. **cautiously**: with great care.

blended: mixed together.
leesten: listen.
summons: calling.
entered the room: note the direct object with *to enter*. **step**: pace. **held out**: extended.
to repulse him: to drive him backwards. **he sank**: he sat.
beside: next to. **bowing**: bending.
amazement: great surprise.
dispense with: do without.
would rather: would prefer.

calls: appointments.
painful: sorrowful.
ease: relax.
ill-used: abused; cruelly treated.

wound: hurt.

I care nothing: I am not interested. **clear**: take the guilt away from.

73

"Let me tell you, then, the train of reasoning which passed through my mind in Baker Street. The idea of a vampire was to me absurd. Such things do not happen in criminal practice in England. And yet your observation was precise. You had seen the lady rise from beside the child's cot with the blood upon her lips".

"I did".

"Did it not occur to you that a bleeding wound may be sucked for some other purpose than to draw the blood from it? Was there not a queen in English history who sucked such a wound to draw poison from it?"

"Poison!"

"A South American household. My instinct felt the presence of those weapons upon the wall before my eyes ever saw them. It might have been other poison, but that was what occured to me. When I saw that little empty quiver beside the small bird-bow, it was just what I expected to see. If the child were pricked with one of those arrows dipped in curare or some other devilish drug, it would mean death if the venom were not sucked out.

"And the dog! If one were to use such a poison would one not try it first in order to see that it had not lost its power? I did not foresee the dog, but at least I understand him and he fitted into my reconstruction.

"Now do you understand? Your wife feared such an attack. She saw it made and saved the child's life, and yet she shrank from telling you all the truth, for she knew how you lovcd the boy and feared lest it break your heart".

"Jacky!"

"I watched him as you fondled the child just now. His face was clearly reflected in the glass of the window where the shutter formed a background. I saw such jealousy, such cruel hatred, as I have seldom seen in a human face."

"My Jacky!"

"You have to face it, Mr. Ferguson. It is the more painful because it is a distorted love, a manical exaggerated love for you, and possibly for his dead mother, which has prompted his action. His very soul is consumed with

74

train: sequence.

to me: in my opinion.

rise: stand up. **beside**: next to. **cot**: little bed.

Did it not occur to you: did you not think.
purpose: reason. **to draw**: to extract.

household: family.
upon: (archaic) on.

occured to me: came to my mind. **quiver**: container for arrows.
beside: next to. **bird-bow**: bow to hunt birds.
if the child were: *subjunctive*. **pricked**: wounded.
dipped: immersed. **curare**: very strong poison.

were to use: had to use.

foresee: thought in advance of.
he fitted into: he conformed to.

shrank: felt great reluctance. **for**: because.
lest it break: that it would break.

as: when. **you fondled**: you cuddled; you treated with great affection.
shutter: door window.
hatred: enmity. **seldom**: rarely.

to face it: to accept it. **painful**: sorrowful.

prompted: caused.

hatred for this splendid child, whose health and beauty are a contrast to his own weakness".

"Good God! It is incredible!"

"Have I spoken the truth, madame?"

The lady was sobbing, with her face buried in the pillows. Now she turned to her husband.

"How could I tell you, Bob? I felt the blow it would be to you. It was better that I should wait and that it should come from some other lips than mine. When this gentleman, who seems to have powers of magic, wrote that he knew all, I was glad".

"I think a year at sea would be my prescription for Master Jacky", said Holmes, rising from his chair. "Only one thing is still clouded, madame. We can quite understand your attacks upon Master Jacky. There is a limit to a mother's patience. But how did you dare to leave the child these last two days?"

"I had told Mrs. Mason. She knew".

"Exactly. So I imagined ".

Ferguson was standing by the bed, choking, his hands outstretched and quivering.

"This, I fancy, is the time for our exit, Watson", said Holmes in a whisper. "If you will take one elbow of the too faithful Dolores, I will take the other. There, now", he added as he closed the door behind him, "I think we may leave them to settle the rest among themselves".

I have only one further note to this case. It is the letter which Holmes wrote in final answer to that with which the narrative begins. It ran thus:

Baker Street,
Nov. 21ˢᵗ

Re Vampires

Sir:

Referring to your letter of the 19ᵗʰ, I beg to state that I have looked into the inquiry of your client, Mr. Robert

hatred: enmity.

sobbing: crying.
turned to: talked to.
blow: stroke.

glad: happy; very pleased.
a year at sea: a year on a boat. **prescription**: remedy. **Master**: formal address for a young boy. **rising**: standing up.
clouded: not clear.

how did you dare: how did you have the courage.

by the bed: next to the bed. **choking**: suffocating.
outstretched: extended. **quivering**: trembling.
I fancy: I think.
in a whisper: in a very low voice.

to settle: to arrange.
further: more.

narrative: story. **It ran this**: this is what it said.

Re: reference; content of the letter.

I have looked into: I have examined.

Ferguson, of Ferguson and Muirhead, tea brokers, of Mincing Lane, and that the matter has become brought to satisfactory conclusion. With thanks for your recommendation,

I am, sir,

Faithfully yours
SHERLOCK HOLMES.

COMPREHENSION QUESTIONS

1) Why did Morrison, Morrison and Dodd pass the matter of vampires to Holmes?

2) Does Holmes take the matter seriously at first? Why? Why not?

3) When does he change his mind?

4) How had the Peruvian lady behaved towards her stepson and baby?

5) What caused the nurse to tell her employer about the matter?

6) What was the husband's first reaction?

7) Did the lady explain her behavior?

8) Describe Robert Ferguson.

9) In what way is Jack a cripple?

10) Why does Holmes decide to go to Lamberly?

11) Is Holmes busy on other cases at the moment?

12) Did Jack get on well with his stepmother before she attacked him?

13) How does his father describe Jack's character?

14) Describe Ferguson's house. Would you say it is an attractive house? Why? Why not?

15) Which decorations particularly arouse Holmes' interest?

16) What is wrong with the dog?

17) Why does Ferguson accuse Holmes of playing with him?

18) Why does Dolores take Watson to see the lady?

19) What does Watson think is wrong with the lady?

20) Why does the lady think her love is greater than her husband's?

21) Why does she not want to see her husband?

tea brokers: importers of tea.

matter: affair. ***has become brought***: has been brought.

---

22) What is the only thing she wants?
23) Why does her husband not trust her with her baby?
24) Describe Jack's appearance.
25) How does he behave towards his father?
26) How does Watson know Jack suffered from a weak back?
27) What does Watson think Holmes is staring at with such an intent expression?
28) What was the baby's nurse like?
29) Does Holmes think Ferguson's case is complicated?
30) When and how had Holmes reached his conclusions?
31) Why did he come to Ferguson's house if he had already solved the mystery?
32) How does Holmes gain entry to the lady's room?
33) What was the lady's reaction to his note?
34) How does Holmes describe his method of revealing the mystery to Ferguson?
35) Had Holmes ever taken the vampire theory seriously?
36) How and why had the dog been hurt?
37) How had the lady saved the baby's life?
38) Why had the lady not told her husband about the attack on the baby?
39) What expression did Holmes see on Jack's face while his father was fondling the baby?
40) How had he seen this expression?
41) What had caused Jack's action?
42) Why did he particularly hate the baby?
43) What does Holmes think would benifit Jack?
44) How did the lady ensure the baby's safety while she was closed in her room?

Without looking back at the text, choose the correct answers - a., b., c. or d..

1) I was engaged in clearing .... some small points in connection with it.
   a. up   **b.** out   **c.** into   **d.** in

2) He would do nothing, and .... saying that there was no harm done.
   a. kept on   **b.** kept up   **c.** took up   **d.** kept in

3) The cabman said he could not imagine what .... of him, for he had seen him get in.
   a. has become   **b.** becomes **c.** had become   **d.** is becoming

4) You are .... wonderfully. You have really done very well.
   a. coming along   **b.** setting out   **c.** taking up   **d.** putting up

5) Let me just .... the course of events, and you will contradict me if I go wrong.
   a. run in   **b.** run over   **c.** run up   **d.** run away with

6) The case has, in some respects, been not entirely .... interest.
   a. missing   **b.** lacking of   **c.** losing   **d.** devoid of

7) He turned .... the pages with eagerness.
   a. out   **b.** up   **c.** over   **d.** in

8) The nurse's nerve had ....; she could stand the strain no longer.
   a. taken away   **b.** given way   **c.** put away **d.** got away

9) She rushed to her room and locked herself in. .... she has refused to see me.
   a. Even if   **b.** Since   **c.** Since then **d.** Although

10) She raised a pair of frightened but beautiful eyes and .... me in apprehension.
   a. glared at   **b.** glimpsed   **c.** looked for   **d.** stared

11) Following his gaze I could only guess that he was looking .... the window at the melancholy, dripping garden.
   a. past   **b.** up to   **c.** out through   **d.** into

12) I care nothing .... you clear my wife. Everything on earth is insignificant compared to that.
   a. so long as   **b.** even if   **c.** although   **d.** however